PERSONAL FITNESS:
LOOKING GOOD FEELING GOOD

CHARLES S. WILLIAMS
University of Florida

EMMANOUEL G. HARAGEONES
Escambia County Schools, Florida

DEWAYNE J. JOHNSON
Florida State University

CHARLES D. SMITH
University of South Florida

Third Edition

KENDALL/HUNT PUBLISHING COMPANY
4050 Westmark Drive P.O. Box 1840 Dubuque, Iowa 52004-1840

CONTENTS

PREFACE

This book could be one of the most meaningful books you will read while in school. Our primary goal with this book is to help people help themselves. It is important that we help you assume control and responsibility for your lifestyle. This book will help you better understand your personal capabilities from a physical fitness standpoint and will enable you to use basic knowledge about the effects of nutrition and stress management, as well as exercise, in establishing a personal fitness program.

If physical activity can be incorporated into your lifestyle in an appropriate manner, there is no question it will enhance your physical appearance. When you are able to enhance your physical appearance, you will also enhance how you feel about yourself. That is what this book is all about, guiding you to help yourself **look and feel better.** It is important to remember that there are certain factors over which you have no control. These factors, which are hereditary traits, include height, bone structure, type of body build, and facial features. Beyond these factors, however, you do have control over what you can be like in a physical sense.

We believe that *looking good and feeling good* are of great importance to everyone. We also believe that the vast majority of people can improve their bodies in terms of fitness. When that occurs, bodies become more attractive, resulting in people feeling good about themselves. If we improve our bodies in some way, we will have taken control of that part of our life, and we will gain a sense of achievement and self-confidence. We will have accomplished something important to us that was not easy. An important thing to remember is that when you do achieve improvement physically, you will be affected in more than just a physical way.

Since we are very complex beings, something that affects one aspect of our lives will likewise affect other dimensions of our lives. If people want to lose weight, and do lose a few pounds, they gain a sense of pride because they made something happen. In other words, they were in control of themselves and in control of part of their life. What happens when people are successful? They are much more likely to be successful again. There is an old saying, *nothing succeeds like success.* This book is designed to help **you** be successful.

Our intent and commitment is to motivate you to become physically active. More importantly, we want you to develop an attitude that values participation in meaningful physical activity. We believe strongly in your ability to take charge of the health and physical fitness aspects of your life. Good luck in your pursuit of self-improvement.

Charles S. Williams
Emmanouel G. Harageones
Dewayne J. Johnson
Charles D. Smith

LOOKING GOOD
FEELING GOOD 1

Chapter Objectives

As you read this chapter, look for answers to these key questions:

- Why is physical fitness a personal matter?
- What are the primary health risk factors and which ones may be controlled?
- What benefits are gained by exercising?
- Why do some people neglect their health by choosing not to participate in physical activity?

When you have completed this chapter, you should understand the meaning of these vocabulary terms:

diabetes
fad
trend
media
physical fitness
health risk factors
inactivity
obesity
cholesterol
body image

Personal Fitness Is a Personal Matter

Success does not mean being the best, but doing your best.

Do you know anyone who doesn't want to look as good as possible or to feel as good as possible? Probably not. It is simply human nature to want to look and feel good. A fascinating fact is that everyone has a great deal of control over this desire. While you inherit your body type from your parents and grandparents, you can control your feelings and attitudes about yourself. One of the biggest factors which determines how you feel about yourself is your body. If you are pleased with the condition of your body, then chances are you will feel good about yourself totally.

Personal fitness is a PERSONAL matter. The word PERSONAL is a key point to remember. Try not to compare yourself to anyone else in any way when working on self-improvement in physical fitness. Take PRIDE in seeing yourself improve throughout this course. One of the most important things that will help you to experience success in improving how you look and feel is your ATTITUDE. Try to keep an open mind about personal fitness. Do not let others influence you in a negative way. Always try your best and give 100 percent. If you let others influence you in the wrong way, you will be the *loser*. Keeping a positive attitude can make a tremendous difference in almost any dimension of your life. That is certainly true when it comes to personal fitness.

"Hi. We hope you are tuned in to improving your bodies. Being in good physical shape can mean a lot to all of us. See you at the end of the book."

Physical Fitness Is a Trend

During the past fifteen years, there has been a remarkable awakening of interest in personal fitness. Walkers, joggers, roller bladers, and bikers move through parks and along highways. Tennis and racquetball courts are filled, as are swimming pools. Health clubs and fitness centers are extremely popular. You undoubtedly have many friends who are on personal fitness programs. Physical activity should be an important ingredient in everyone's lifestyle.

There was a time when a lot of people would get excited about some form of exercise and would do it very regularly for a period of time but would then lose enthusiasm and stop. That is called a **FAD.** However, interest in physical fitness has persisted for many years and continues to be part of many people's lifestyles. When the interest in something, such as physical fitness, lasts for a long time, it is called a **TREND.** Physical fitness continues to be a TREND in this country. This is great news since personal fitness is such an important aspect of achieving greater self-respect and of moving closer to and expanding your overall potential.

Many people are excited about their physical fitness programs and have active lifestyles. However, research studies continue to show that a large percentage of adults are not very fit and are overweight and out of shape. Are any members of your family inactive and overweight? Studies also show that a fairly large percentage of teens are in rather poor condition and that many have a negative attitude toward physical fitness. If you or any of your friends are in this category, this personal fitness course will give you an opportunity to start building a healthier lifestyle. That can be a rewarding process.

What Affects Your Attitude Toward Physical Fitness?

Since *feeling good* about your body is such an important part of your self image and self concept, why do some people have a negative attitude toward the very thing which can help them improve their bodies? Several answers to this question will be discussed here, and you may have a couple of others as well.

Lack of athletic ability

Due to a lack of understanding of physical fitness, many people think that being a fast runner or a good ballplayer is part of physical fitness. With this type of thinking, many students who do not have a broad athletic background feel as though they cannot become physically fit. This way of thinking is unfortunate because *you do not have to be a skilled person to be physically fit.* You will find that your experience in this course will be personally satisfying.

Past experience with youth sports

A second reason for the possible development of negative attitudes toward physical fitness is youth sports. It is estimated that over 20 million young people, ages 5 to 16, play youth sports in this country. Youth sports have been and still are great experiences for many participants. However, there is another side to this story, one which is not so positive. A high percentage of young athletes, both male and female, drop out of youth sports at a relatively early age. The main reason some players begin to feel inferior to others is that the pressure to win increases and they stop having fun. Adolescent psychologists believe many young people develop a negative attitude toward their physical selves, and this may carry over into attitudes toward their capabilities.

Heredity plays a role

We belong to a society which rewards slimness and athletic ability to a high degree. It is difficult to define what is meant by the ideal body shape. Many young women believe they should look like Miss America. The *thin is in* attitude exists. Young men are typically expected to have lean, muscular bodies. As you are aware, very few people have the figure or body shape they perceive as being ideal.

It is very important for you to understand the role *heredity* plays in a person's final body type or build. Bone structure influences a person's measurements. Naturally a person with large bones will have larger measurements than a person with small bones. However, people with either large or small bone structures can have attractive body shapes, even though their measurements vary greatly. Regardless of your body type, the one key fact to keep in mind is that you can maximize the attractiveness of your body through a proper physical fitness program.

Heredity plays a role in your body type.

Media influence

Another factor that may foster negative attitudes about physical fitness in the minds of teens is the **media** coverage in magazines, television, and newspapers ads. While the media has drawn unusual positive attention to many aspects of health and fitness, there have also been some negative aspects. People who sell items to improve appearance frequently do so in a very tricky manner. They suggest that every young woman should have a slender and attractive body and every young man should have a muscular and well-shaped body. It is unfortunate that some young people will not attain these levels of excellence from an appearance standpoint and, consequently, will develop feelings of inadequacy in relation to their bodies. Along the same line, some parents are also influenced by the media in terms of what young people should look like. As a result, they sometimes put pressure on their children to lose weight or to do something else to improve their appearance. The following section explains reasons why some people cannot attain the standards which are promoted in the media.

Confused about physical fitness?

SPEED?
POWER?
AGILITY?
BODY FAT?
CARDIOVASCULAR?
COORDINATION?
BALANCE?
STRENGTH?
FLEXIBILITY?
MUSCULAR ENDURANCE?
REACTION TIME?

The smile tells the story. It is obvious she likes what the scale says.

What Is Physical Fitness?

Definitions of physical fitness vary widely. It is easy to understand why many people are confused about physical fitness. To some people, having a high level of physical fitness means being a good athlete. It is true that most athletes are in very good shape; however, one does not have to be skillful to be physically fit.

Body weight can be misleading

Today there seems to be a *slimness mania,* especially for females. Individuals with this attitude frequently measure physical fitness by the bathroom scale. In other words, if the scale reports that the person weighs just what she wants to weigh, she is very happy. If, on the other hand, the scale reports a reading which is five pounds over the desired weight, the individual is very unhappy. This is an unfortunate misconception about physical fitness. Being obese is without question a factor that works against being physically fit, but many young people believe they are physically fit just because their weight is at a desirable level. Do you know anyone who is very slender yet is in terrible physical condition? Being at an appropriate weight is just one aspect of physical fitness, but it in no way indicates that a person is physically fit.

Some people have an obsession about being too fat, and in struggling to control their weight, they may be depriving themselves of important nutrients. The myth that thinness means fitness has been promoted by the various media, and unfortunately they have been very successful. This course will help you take a closer look at the myths and fallacies which surround being physically fit.

Physical fitness defined

Teenagers are concerned with looking good and feeling good, so it is essential that you understand physical fitness. People are described as being physically fit when they are able to carry out daily tasks without undue fatigue, are able to handle emergency situations, and possess sufficient energy to enjoy leisure-time pursuits. **Physical fitness** is determined by the condition of your heart and circulatory system, respiratory system, muscular system, degree of flexibility, and percentage of body fat.

Primary Health Risk Factors

You can significantly change your current health, as well as your future health, by controlling certain **health risk factors** associated with disease, disability, or premature death. The removal of even one of these risk factors may reduce the threat of several diseases. Although you may feel these risk factors are only relevant to older people, maybe those your parent's age, they are quite important to you as well. Since many of these diseases start when a person is a teenager, it is to your benefit to learn how you can control these factors. The most commonly identified risk factors are discussed below.

inactivity

How much time do you sit watching television?

Those who remain active have fewer heart problems and other diseases than those who remain inactive. **Inactivity** limits your chances of being in charge of your life, since physical health is vitally important to your total development. Being physically active also helps you to feel good about yourself.

obesity

Having excessive deposits of fat in the body is called **obesity.** These fatty deposits put a strain on your heart and circulatory system, as well as on all other systems of your body. It has also been reported that obese individuals may have a hard time adjusting socially and emotionally. Obesity, or the initial stages of obesity, typically begin in childhood. Many people are unable to break this trend during their school years and therefore end up as obese adults.

high blood pressure

This condition has been identified as a major cause of heart and other circulatory problems. You probably know people, your parents or their friends, who have high blood pressure. It is important to understand that high blood pressure does not just occur in older people. Many people your age have high blood pressure, caused largely by the stresses of home life, school work, and peer pressure.

high levels of cholesterol

Cholesterol is a waxy, fat-like substance found in the cells. Although cholesterol is needed by the body, diets high in saturated fat can cause cholesterol levels to become too high. When this occurs, the cholesterol may collect in blood vessels and clog them. This is why high levels of cholesterol in the blood frequently are associated with heart disease.

The average American consumes a diet which is extremely high in fat content. While foods at fast food businesses are very tasty, they are generally very high in fat content and, therefore, can increase your cholesterol level.

stress and tension

Unnecessary stress and tension can place a strain on the heart and circulatory system and may lead to various types of diseases. An argument with a close friend may cause you to experience unusual anger, doubt, fear, and similar emotions, which in turn will have a negative effect on your body. Who has not been upset at a parent, teacher, or friend? What happened to your body? Wasn't it *"revved up"* or ready for action, as evidenced by a rapid heart beat and rapid rate of breathing? Adolescence is a very trying time for many teenagers. In fact, the early teen years may be the most difficult time in the lives of many people.

smoking

You have undoubtedly heard about the negative health effects of smoking on your body. It has been firmly established that smoking causes many problems in the circulatory and respiratory systems of your body. The Federal Drug Administration has declared the nicotine contained in tobacco to be addictive. You are *100%* in control of this risk factor.

Who said teenagers' lives were easy?

sex of individual

In the past, men have had a higher rate of heart disease than women. The primary reason for this was because men were more affected by the pressures and stresses of the business world. However, the gap appears to be narrowing since more women are entering the work force and experiencing the same pressures and tension. The increased number of women smoking may also be a factor.

heredity

If you have family members who have had heart attacks or other circulatory problems, your chances of having heart problems increase. In other words, you not only inherit your parents' and grandparents' physical characteristics, but you may also tend to develop the same diseases.

age

While it is true the risk of heart disease increases as one gets older, steps can be taken now to reduce the rate of increase. For example, just because you get older does not mean you should become inactive, nor does it give you an excuse for gaining excessive amounts of weight.

Six of the nine health risk factors can be controlled. Are you a good lion tamer in your own life?

Contributing Health Risk Factor

A contributing risk factor that is not as important as smoking or high blood pressure is diabetes. However, the American Heart Association considers diabetes a contributing risk factor and should not be ignored. **Diabetes** is the inability of the body to produce or use insulin. Insulin is necessary for the body to utilize glucose (sugar).

Without insulin, glucose absorption by the cells and liver is low, leading to high glucose levels in the blood. It is estimated that 80% of diabetics die with some form of heart or blood vessel disease. Changes in eating habits, weight control, exercise habits, and drug therapy are often used to keep diabetes under control.

Benefits of Exercise

What's in it for you? The answer to this question is highly personal, and you may believe some of the benefits which will be discussed are not very meaningful to you. We want to assure you they are all true.

Improved appearance

Looking as good as possible is very important to everyone, particularly to people your age. Exercise and fitness activities help control body weight and help make your body more attractive. Many music stars, actresses, and actors are very concerned about their appearance and consequently follow well-designed fitness programs. Exercise helps to tone muscles and shape your body.

Both young men and women can benefit from muscular strength and endurance exercises.

If you improve your personal physical appearance, there is a great likelihood you will also improve the way you feel about yourself, in an overall sense. This also creates a positive cycle in your life. As you improve your physical appearance, your feelings about yourself improve. When you feel good about yourself, the chances are greater that you will want to continue to improve yourself, not just in a physical way but in all aspects.

Improved body image

Body image means the way you see your physical self. Are you pleased when you look into a full length mirror? Since many people do not like their body images, properly designed fitness programs may be just the answer for them. Remember, your body image is just one part of your self-concept. Improving your body image can also improve the total way in which you see yourself and feel about yourself.

Do you like what you see in the mirror? Is the mirror a friend or foe?

Improved self-control

People who take control of their bodies and their lifestyles generally experience less stress and depression than those who are indifferent to striving for personal improvement. Having control of this aspect of your life may also help you have greater feelings of self-confidence, regardless of the situations in which you find yourself.

More enjoyment of life

While many people your age enjoy life a great deal, there are still many who, for one reason or another, have a lot of pressure and stress in their lives. Exercise will not only provide relief from daily anxieties, it can also have a refreshing, exhilarating effect on your life.

Improved health

Physical activity beyond the daily routine is needed to avoid heart disease and other illnesses associated with inactivity. This is particularly true for older people, but it also has relevance for you. Active people are also healthier because their digestion is enhanced through exercise and there is better elimination of waste products from the body.

Increased muscular strength and endurance

The vast majority of male teenagers are anxious to be as strong as possible and to have well-developed muscles. While the majority of female teenagers do not want to develop large muscles, they do want to have firm, well-toned bodies. In both cases, the end result will be improved personal appearance. This leads directly to the next benefit of exercise.

Increased level of energy

Being tired during the day may be the direct result of poor lifestyle choices, such as poor nutritional and rest habits. Low energy may also be due to a body that is not tuned-up appropriately. Your body might be equated to an expensive car. How many people would put cheap gas in a fancy sports car or disregard all company recommendations for handling it?

A person's body is much more valuable than the most expensive car, yet it is strange that people sometimes disregard the key guidelines for getting the maximum performance from it. Appropriate exercise activities are a key factor in helping your body function near an optimal level. A *higher energy level* is one outcome of following an exercise program. A high level of fitness will prevent fatigue and allow you to enjoy leisure-time activities to a high degree.

Is your body as important as a car? Do you know people who take better care of their cars than they do of their bodies?

Improved physical performance

You will not fatigue as quickly, and thus you can play longer, gain more skill, and therefore experience a greater degree of success. You will also be able to complete your school day without a high degree of fatigue. Someone once said, "*Fatigue makes cowards of us all.*" Whether that is a true statement or not is not important. The point to be kept in mind is that fatigue or a low energy level definitely keeps you from performing near your optimal level.

Increased success in your school work or job

Ancient Greeks used a phrase that summed up their belief about the importance of the body: **a sound mind in a sound body.** This was what they thought was essential in the education of their children. Research studies show that increased fitness helps with academic achievement. As your body becomes more efficient, you simply function more effectively overall.

Helps cope with stress

Teenagers are under many stresses today and frequently become depressed, angry, or anxious about their lives. A good exercise program can be one of the most important ways to deal with stress. In Chapter 11, you will learn several easy techniques for recognizing and handling the stress in your life.

Improved physical fitness helps to ward off fatigue.

Sleep better

For the majority of you, sleeping may not be a problem. However, this is not the case for some people. Exercise relieves tension, and so your body relaxes more, enabling you to go to sleep more quickly and to sleep soundly.

Increased life expectancy

This benefit may seem to be more related to your parents or some older friends than to you. Remember the comparison of your body to an expensive car? The car motor will last much longer if it is cared for properly, and so will your body. Many diseases attributed to in-activity begin at an early age because people disregard the needs of their bodies and abuse them.

Physical fitness activities provide almost immediate physical and mental benefits. The physical benefits include all that go *with looking good and feeling good* about yourself. The mental benefits include increased self-esteem, improved self-control, and a feeling of confidence.

Can you think of other benefits? The key point to remember is that there are many benefits of exercise for everyone, especially for people your age.

Summary

There is no easy path to physical fitness. Many people would like you to believe there is, because they can make millions of dollars from your purchases. It is a fantasy to think you can take a magic pill, or do a two-minute-a-day exercise schedule and become fit. If you wish to gain, regain, or maintain a high level of personal physical well-being, you must be prepared to give time and effort to attain your goals.

To be successful at this task, you need to answer the following questions honestly:

1. Are you satisfied with your present state of physical fitness?
2. Are you satisfied with your "body image" (what the mirror says)?
3. Does your lifestyle include vigorous physical activity?
4. Could you improve your lifestyle?

If you answered no to any of these questions, you should recognize the need for engaging in a personal fitness program. **The challenge is yours. Go for it.**

You have a choice!

Study Questions

True–false

Circle "T" for all correct statements and "F" for all incorrect ones.

T   F   1. Setting up a personal physical fitness program may provide both physical and mental benefits.

T   F   2. The way people look has little effect on how they feel about themselves.

T   F   3. During the past 15 years, there has been a remarkable increase of interest in physical fitness.

T   F   4. Teenagers are less concerned about their appearance than older people.

T   F   5. The media is one reason some people have negative attitudes toward their own bodies.

T   F   6. A person does not need to be an athlete to be very healthy and physically fit.

T   F   7. Physical fitness deals with five factors: cardiovascular fitness, muscular strength, muscular endurance, flexibility, and body composition.

T   F   8. "Body image" means the way you see your physical self.

T   F   9. Improving your physical fitness level has nothing to do with your energy level.

T   F   10. Taking control of their bodies and lifestyles may help people experience less stress and depression.

Risk factor checklist

Nine risk factors determine how well you can look and feel. Check the space **"I can control"** or **"I cannot control"** beside the following risk factors. For example, age is a factor that cannot be controlled. Therefore, place a check in the "I CANNOT CONTROL" column.

	I CAN CONTROL	I CANNOT CONTROL
11. Inactivity		
12. Obesity		
13. High Blood Pressure		
14. High Levels of Cholesterol		
15. Stress and Tension		
16. Smoking		
17. Sex of Individual		
18. Heredity		
19. Age		

Discussion

20. In what way is physical fitness related to body image?

21. In your opinion, what effect can advertisements seen in magazines and on television have on the way people see themselves physically?

22. Why is the word "*personal*" so important in a personal fitness class?

23. Compare two people your age, one who is very fit and one who is rather unfit. Are there any differences in them besides physical fitness?

24. What is the relationship, if any, between body image and self esteem?

COMPONENTS OF FITNESS **2**

Chapter Objectives

As you read this chapter, look for answers to these key questions:

- What is the difference between health-related and skill-related physical fitness?

- What are the health-related components of physical fitness?

- What are the skill-related components of physical fitness?

- Why does a person not have to be a good athlete to be physically fit?

- Why is it important to know your current level of health-related fitness?

When you have completed this chapter, you should understand the meaning of these vocabulary terms:

skill-related fitness	balance
health-related fitness	power
flexibility	reaction time
cardiovascular fitness	coordination
muscular strength	speed
muscular endurance	norm-referenced tests
body composition	criterion-referenced tests
agility	health-related fitness standards

Analyzing Physical Fitness

If it is to be, it is up

to me.

There has been a lot of confusion centered on the questions "What is physical fitness?" and "How can it be attained?" It is very important that you understand the answers to these questions if you are going to be responsible for your own health and fitness.

Physical fitness is made up of both health-related and skill-related components. The **skill-related fitness** items are factors which relate to the possibility of your becoming a good athlete. Are you fast? Do you have good eye-hand coordination? The **health-related fitness** components relate to how well the systems of your body operate. Are your heart and other muscles of your body in good shape? This type of physical fitness is related to your overall state of health. The focus of this book will be on the health-related components of physical fitness, why they are important, and how each can be improved.

Health-Related Fitness

Both kinds of fitness are important to successful participation in sports activities. However, only the health-related components, if adequately developed, can contribute toward the prevention of disease and the promotion of health. These components are essential to good health and fitness. That is why they are called health-related.

Maintaining an acceptable level of the health-related components of physical fitness is recognized as a key element of a healthy lifestyle. People who attain such levels of fitness reduce their risks of developing certain health problems, such as heart disease, low back pain, and obesity, and improve their body's ability to function. This is why health-related fitness should be of utmost concern to everyone.

There are five *health-related components of physical fitness:* flexibility, cardiovascular fitness, muscular strength, muscular endurance, and body composition. Remember, fitness is for everyone. You do not have to be a good athlete to be physically fit. If you exercise regularly and follow basic training principles, you will improve your health-related fitness.

Flexibility

Flexibility means the range of movement possible at various joints. This component of fitness is probably the most frequently overlooked. People can get along without being very flexible, particularly if they are inactive and do not wish to operate near their maximum potential. If you want to be as good as you can be, you must work on your flexibility just as regularly as you do your muscular strength and endurance or your cardiovascular efficiency.

Because flexibility is specific to each joint, no single test will provide complete information about the flexibility of all major joints of your body. However, there are several tests that will give you an indication of flexibility in joints most likely needing attention. Flexibility of your lower back and posterior thighs can be evaluated using the sit-and-reach test.

The sit-and-reach test measures flexibility.

Sit-and-Reach Test

Procedures:

1. Warm-up prior to testing.

2. Remove your shoes and sit at the test box with your legs fully extended.

3. Place your feet shoulder-width apart and flat against the test box.

4. Slide your arms forward with palms down and one hand on top of the other.

5. As a partner places his or her hands on your knees to keep them from bending, reach forward, sliding your fingertips as far forward along the ruler as possible and hold that position for one second. Do not bounce or rock forward.

6. Have your partner measure the distance your fingertips reach to the nearest centimeter.

7. Four trials are allowed with the best reach being recorded.

Cardiovascular fitness

Cardiovascular fitness deals with the ability of the heart, blood, blood vessels, and the respiratory system to supply oxygen and necessary fuel to the muscles during exercise. The best type of exercise for improving cardiovascular fitness is aerobic exercise. *Aerobic exercises* are those activities which force the body to use a large amount of oxygen for a sustained period of time. Sustained means the exercise should be done for at least 15–30 minutes to get the important benefits. Examples of aerobic exercises are jogging, cycling, swimming, rope jumping, and aerobic dance. Certain sports activities, such as basketball and soccer, also provide the type of demand needed to achieve an aerobic training effect. Aerobic exercise is a very important key to safeguarding both your physical and mental health.

You may run for distance or time to measure aerobic endurance.

Cardiovascular fitness can be measured in a number of ways. The most accurate measurement is a stress test performed on a stationary bicycle or treadmill in a physical fitness laboratory or hospital. This test requires expensive equipment and highly trained personnel. Cardio-vascular fitness can be more easily evaluated with distance runs and step tests. The most common distance runs are the one-mile run and the one-and-a-half-mile run for time and the nine-minute run and the twelve-minute run for distance. Prior to doing a distance run, you should practice running to learn how to pace yourself. It is also important to condition yourself before attempting a timed run.

One-Mile Run

Procedures:

1. Warm-up prior to testing.

2. Start the timer and cover the one-mile distance as fast as possible.

3. Use the fastest pace that you can sustain for the entire one-mile distance.

4. You may walk if you have to; however, the goal is to cover the one mile in the shortest time possible.

5. After you have covered the one mile, stop the timer and record the time (minutes and seconds) it took you to cover this distance.

6. Cool-down after testing.

Muscular strength and muscular endurance

Muscular strength and endurance are two components which are very closely related and are of extreme importance to teenagers. **Muscular strength** is the ability of muscles to exert a force one time. **Muscular endurance** is the ability to use muscles for long periods of time.

In the past, young men were much more interested in muscular development than young women were. That gap is closing rapidly as more and more women are realizing the importance of improving their muscles. Today, women are more anxious than ever before to have firm and well-toned bodies. The important fact to remember is that most females do not have and will not develop large muscles for the simple reason that they do not have enough of the necessary hormones. Young men, on the other hand, have a higher level of the male hormone (*testosterone*), enabling them to greatly increase muscle size and definition. Remember, regardless of whether you are male or female, by improving your muscular development, you will also be improving your body image.

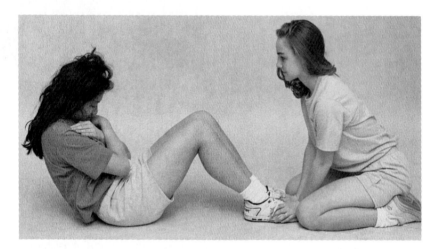

Sit-ups and crunches measure abdominal muscular strength and endurance.

Abdominal muscular strength and endurance can be easily measured by performance of sit-ups for a one-minute time period. Pull-ups, push-ups, and parallel bar dips are commonly used to evaluate arm and shoulder girdle muscular strength and endurance.

Sit-Up Test

Procedures:

1. Warm-up prior to testing.

2. Lie flat on your back with your knees bent, feet on the floor, and heels 12 to 18 inches from your buttocks.

3. Cross your arms and place them across your chest with your hands on opposite shoulders.

4. Have your partner hold your feet to keep them in contact with the floor.

5. Curl up to a sitting position, keeping your arms in contact with your chest. A sit-up is completed when your elbows touch your thighs. Return to the down position by uncurling until your mid-back makes contact with the floor.

6. Perform as many sit-ups as you can in one minute.

7. Cool-down after testing.

Pull-ups measure upper body muscular strength and endurance.

Pull-Up Test

Procedures:

1. Warm-up prior to testing.
2. With your arms straight, hang from a bar with the palms of your hands facing away from your body.
3. Pull your body upward until your chin is lifted over the bar. Return to the starting position.
4. Perform as many pull-ups as possible.
5. No swinging, kicking, or other jerky movements are allowed.
6. Cool-down after testing.

Body composition

Body composition is the ratio of fat to muscle, bone, and other tissues that compose your body. A certain amount of body fat is needed for good health. Extremely high or low amounts of body fat can cause health problems. Most young adults desire a low percentage of body fat. Your **"body image"** may suffer if your percent of body fat is too high. Looking good and feeling good depends a great deal on what percentage of your body weight is fat. Information you gain from this text, if put to practice, will help you to achieve an ideal body weight and an appropriate level of body fat.

Body composition can be evaluated in several ways. *Underwater weighing* and *electrical impedance analysis* are the two most accurate methods of determining what percentage of body weight is fat. However, both methods require expensive equipment and trained personnel. Body composition is more commonly assessed by measuring the thickness of skinfolds. This kind of measurement uses a device called a skinfold caliper. Triceps and calf skinfold measurements provide a good estimate of what percentage of body weight is fat.

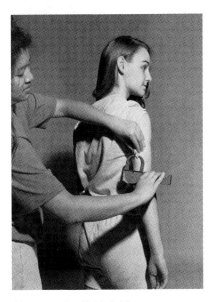 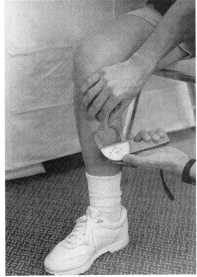

Triceps and calf skinfold measurements assess body composition.

Tricep and Calf Skinfolds

Procedures:

1. Have your partner mark the following two sites with a marking pencil:
   triceps—midpoint between your shoulder and your elbow on the back of your right arm
   calf—inside your right lower leg at the largest part of your calf

2. When measuring your triceps skinfold, stand erect with your right arm relaxed.

3. When measuring your calf skinfold, place your right foot on an elevated surface or sit in a chair so that your knee is bent at a 90-degree angle.

4. Have your partner take the measurements by pinching a fold of your skin between the thumb and forefinger slightly above the mark. Have your partner measure the thickness of the skinfold at the mark by pulling the fold away from the underlying muscle and applying the skinfold caliper to the fold.

5. Have your partner take three consecutive measurements at each site. Read the skinfold to the nearest millimeter. Record the middle of the three scores at each site.

6. Add the middle score of your three triceps measurements to the middle score of your three calf measurements. The sum is your total score.

Skill-Related Fitness

There are six *skill-related components* of physical fitness: agility, balance, power, reaction time, coordination, and speed. These factors contribute toward your ability to successfully participate in sports activities. Regular participation in sports or other recreational pursuits can have a very positive influence on your health and fitness. Individuals who have a higher level of skill-related fitness are more likely to be physically active than those who have a lesser degree of skills.

Agility

Agility is the ability to change the position of your body and to control the movement of your whole body. Agility is a very important quality in many sports, because you must change direction rapidly and always have your body under control.

Agility tests are often the same as or similar to conditioning and practice drills used in various sports. Shuttle runs, zigzag runs, and the hexagonal jump are some examples of ways to measure agility.

The zigzag run may be used to measure agility.

Balance

Balance is the ability to keep an upright posture while either standing still or moving. Good balance is essential to be successful in activities such as ice skating, skiing, surfing, and gymnastics.

Many challenging tasks can be used to evaluate balance. Some examples are standing on the ball of one foot as long as possible, standing on such objects as a balance board or roller board with one or both feet as long as possible, walking on a balance beam, and doing head and handstands.

Standing on one foot can be used to measure static balance.
Walking on a balance beam is used to measure dynamic balance.

Power

Power is the ability to do strength performances at a rapid pace. Strength and speed are both involved in power. Football players, swimmers, shot putters, discus throwers, and high jumpers are examples of athletes who typically have a high degree of power.

The vertical jump and the standing long jump are commonly used to assess power.

Reaction time

Reaction time is the amount of time it takes to get moving once your senses signal the need to move. People with good reaction time will usually be able to start quickly in track and swimming or react quickly in other sports such as ping pong or karate.

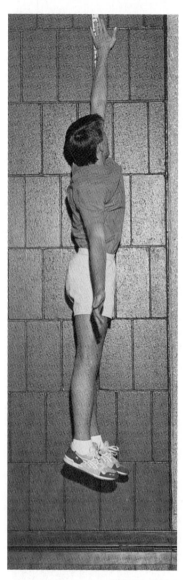

The vertical jump can be used to measure power.

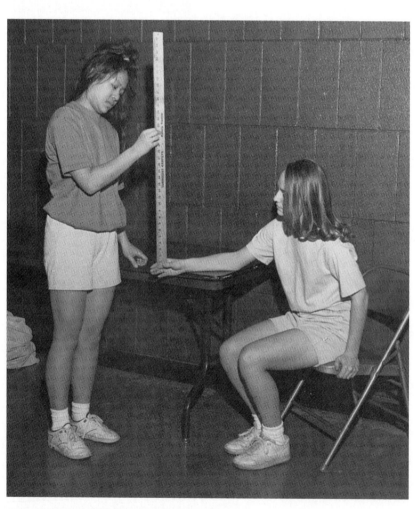

A yardstick may be used to measure reaction time.

A very simple assessment of reaction time is the yardstick test. The object of this test is to catch the yardstick as quickly as possible when it starts to fall. Scoring is based on how far the yardstick falls before being caught.

Coordination

Coordination is the integration of eye, hand, and foot movements. This component is necessary for success in such sports as tennis, golf, and basketball, where good hand-eye coordination is essential.

Like agility, tests of coordination are often the same as or similar to conditioning and practice drills used in various sports. Some examples are dribbling and shooting in basketball, place kicking and punting in football, and dribbling with the feet in soccer.

A ball toss against a wall can be used to measure hand-eye coordination.

Kicking a soccer ball against a wall can be used to measure foot-eye coordination.

Speed

Speed is the ability to cover a distance in a short time. Speed is a very important factor in many sports activities.

Short runs are used to evaluate speed. Examples of such tests are the 50-yard dash and the 100-yard dash. The 40-yard dash is the most frequently used measure of speed in football.

The 50-yard dash can be used to measure speed.

Analyzing Fitness Assessment

Before beginning a personal fitness program, you should know your present level of flexibility, cardiovascular fitness, muscular strength and endurance, and body composition. You should also know how to measure each of these components and how to interpret the assessment results. The health-related fitness tests described in the *Personal Fitness: Looking Good/Feeling Good Activity Handbook* will help you learn how to measure your own fitness level, identify your strengths and weaknesses, and interpret your test results. The first assessment, or pre-test, is to determine your present fitness level and to provide you with a basis for setting realistic goals. The post-test, at the conclusion of the instructional program, will help you determine the progress you made toward your goals and assist you in setting new goals.

Importance of self-testing

Periodic self-testing is an effective way to monitor your progress, determine the effectiveness of your personal fitness program, and re-evaluate and update your previously set goals. This is why it is so important for you to know how to assess yourself and to be able to interpret the results. You are encouraged to self-test anytime you wish to check your progress. Self-testing enables you to determine when and how much to change your personal fitness program and to check your progress toward your desired level of health-related fitness. By repeating the tests from time to time, you will develop a sense of ownership for determining your personal fitness needs and the ability to solve your own fitness problems.

Interpreting Assessment Results

Some physical fitness tests utilize norms to indicate fitness levels. These are called **norm-referenced tests.** Assessment results are indicated in percentile rankings. *Percentile rankings* represent the percentage of individuals of the same age and sex who scored at or below your test score. If, for example, you performed at the 75th percentile, you achieved a score better than 75 percent of those in your age group. Percentile rankings, however, should only be used as an indication of your strengths and weaknesses, not as a method of comparing yourself to other people. Remember, fitness is a personal matter. Compete with yourself, not others.

Percentile Norms for the Mile Run (minutes and seconds)					
Females					
Age	**13**	**14**	**15**	**16**	**17+**
Percentile					
95	7:12	7:20	7:41	7:09	7:30
75	8:20	8:15	8:44	9:02	9:05
50	9:29	9:37	10:07	10:47	9:49
25	10:58	11:45	12:23	13:02	11:30
5	14:57	17:01	16:24	15:32	15:26
Males					
Age	**13**	**14**	**15**	**16**	**17+**
Percentile					
95	6:13	5:53	6:03	5:50	6:03
75	6:54	6:38	6:37	6:30	6:38
50	7:29	7:12	7:16	7:13	7:27
25	8:37	8:04	8:06	8:09	8:28
5	10:25	10:34	10:39	10:42	11:00

Other physical fitness tests use specific standards to judge fitness status. These are called **criterion-referenced tests. Health-related fitness standards** represent satisfactory levels of flexibility, cardiovascular fitness, muscular strength and endurance, and body composition necessary for good health. Achieving these standards is important to good health. Not only will you be less susceptible to various health problems if you attain these standards, but you will also be more likely to feel good and look your best.

Health-Fitness Standards for the Mile Run (minutes and seconds)		
Age	**Females**	**Males**
13	11:00	8:30
14	10:30	8:15
15	10:30	8:00
16	10:30	8:00
17	10:30	8:00
18	10:30	8:00

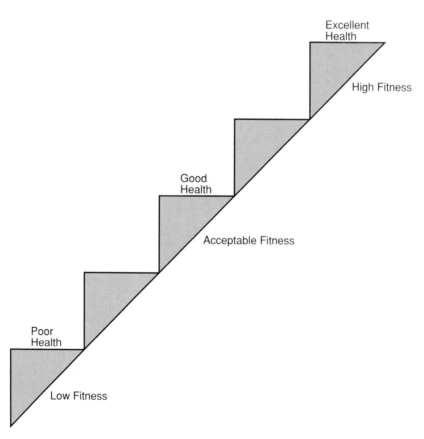

Achieving acceptable health-related fitness standards is important to good health.

Goal Setting

In Chapter 3 you will learn about the importance of goal setting in relation to health and fitness. When you develop your goals, it is essential that you utilize the information regarding your present level of fitness. That is the purpose of the pre-test.

It is important to remember that individuals will improve at different rates. If you score far below the health-related fitness standard in a particular component, you have the potential to make enormous progress in that area. If you score near, at, or above the standard, you may improve only moderately. The more fit you are, the harder you will have to work to make small gains. Less fit individuals might show dramatic improvement, but remain far below their potential. The important thing is to do the best you can. Remember, *fitness is for everyone.*

Summary

There are two kinds of physical fitness: health-related fitness and skill-related fitness. The health-related components are essential to a healthy lifestyle and the prevention of health problems. That is why they are called health-related. The five *health-related fitness components* are flexibility, cardiovascular fitness, muscular strength, muscular endurance, and body composition.

The skill-related components are concerned with abilities related to sports activities. They include agility, balance, power, reaction time, coordination, and speed.

There are several tests to measure each component of physical fitness. Knowledge of how to conduct these tests will allow you to determine your fitness level throughout life. Some physical fitness test results are indicated in percentile rankings and are called norm-referenced tests. Others use specific standards to judge your fitness status and are called criterion-referenced tests.

Before beginning a personal fitness program, you should know your present level of health-related fitness in order to set realistic goals. Self-testing is an effective way to monitor your program. This is why it is crucial that you know how to evaluate yourself and interpret the results.

Physical fitness is for everyone. You do not have to be a good athlete to be physically fit. If you exercise regularly and follow basic training principles, you will improve your health-related fitness.

Study Questions

Matching

Place the letter of the correct answer in the space provided.

_____ 1. Cardiovascular fitness

_____ 2. Aerobic exercises

_____ 3. Health-related fitness components

_____ 4. Skill-related fitness components

_____ 5. Muscular strength and endurance

_____ 6. Flexibility

_____ 7. Body composition

_____ 8. Agility

_____ 9. Power

_____ 10. Reaction time

_____ 11. Coordination

_____ 12. Speed

A. Range of movement possible at various joints

B. Factors related to becoming stronger

C. Factors related to becoming a better athlete

D. Ratio of fat to muscle, bone, and other tissue

E. Ability to change the position of your body and control the movement of your body

F. Ability to cover a distance in a short time

G. Integration of eye, hand, and foot movements

H. Amount of time it takes to get moving

I. Ability to do strength performances at a rapid pace

J. Factors related to how well the systems of your body work

K. Activities which force the body to use a large amount of oxygen for an extended period of time

L. Ability of the circulatory and respiratory systems to supply oxygen to muscles during exercise

Fitness component checklist

Listed below are the components of physical fitness. In the space provided, indicate whether the component is a health-related (HR) or a skill-related (SR) component.

13. _____ Balance

14. _____ Body composition

15. _____ Coordination

16. _____ Speed

17. _____ Muscular strength

18. _____ Muscular endurance

19. _____ Power

20. _____ Flexibility

21. _____ Reaction time

22. _____ Cardiovascular fitness

23. _____ Agility

Discussion

24. What is the difference between health-related fitness and skill-related fitness?

25. Why should everyone be concerned about health-related fitness?

26. What are some tests for assessing each of the health-related components of fitness?

27. Why is it important to know how to assess your own physical fitness level?

28. Describe the difference between norm-referenced tests and criterion-referenced tests.

Chapter Objectives

As you read this chapter, look for answers to these key questions:

- What are goals?
- What is goal setting?
- How can setting goals help you take control of your health and fitness?
- What is the difference between long-term goals and short-term goals?
- What are the steps necessary for successful goal setting?

When you have completed this chapter, you should understand the meaning of these vocabulary terms:

goal setting
long-term goals
short-term goals
time lines

Teen Years: A Topsy-Turvy Time

Nothing can stop people with the right mental attitude from achieving their goals.

Thomas Jefferson

The term "topsy-turvy" means that things are not very certain or established. That is why the term seems appropriate when discussing teenagers. As a teenager, you may agree with this point, or you may be one of the lucky people who is completely happy with every aspect of your life. However, it is true that a large majority of teenagers find this period of time confusing and frustrating. As a teen, you are in a transition from childhood to adulthood. During this transition there are changes occurring in your physical, social, emotional, and mental being. These changes bring both *good* and *not-so-good* experiences. The *good* changes include physical maturation, a sense of independence, the discovery of new abilities, and the satisfaction of taking care of yourself. The *not-so-good* changes include unusual physical differences between peers, moodiness, self-consciousness, discovery of personal limitations, and difficulties involved in taking on new responsibilities.

Teen years bring about both good and not-so-good feelings caused by changes in a person's physical, social, emotional, and mental being.

While the teen years are an emotionally turbulent time, they are also a fantastic time of learning how to take more and more control of your own life. Up until this time in your life, your parents have probably made the vast majority of the decisions on what you ate, what you wore, where you went, who your friends were, and in what activities you were involved. Now you must take more responsibility in making these decisions. Of course, you will still need some guidance from your parents and teachers to help you refine your decision-making ability.

Taking Control of Your Health and Fitness

Now that you have more control over your own life, you also need to accept responsibility for it. Two of the most obvious aspects of your life that need a tremendous amount of attention are your health and fitness. Making responsible decisions on diet, exercise, and the use of your time have an important impact on your lifestyle. As you know, your body image has a direct effect on how you feel about yourself overall. Learning to make appropriate decisions about your personal program of health and fitness behaviors is essential to becoming as happy and as successful as you can be.

Do you have friends who would like to be stronger, weigh a few pounds less, or play some sports activity? Undoubtedly you do. The question therefore arises, if they want these things, why don't they do them? Unfortunately, there is a big gap between wanting something in your life and making it happen. Wouldn't it be nice to just wish for something and have it happen? Who wouldn't like a "money tree" in the backyard? Having a money tree is a wish and not an attainable goal. A realistic goal of having additional spending money will take more than a wish; it will require some effort on your part.

Goal setting must begin with realistic ideas.

One major reason why people are not as healthy and fit as they desire to be is that they have never been taught how to attain this goal. This Personal Fitness course is a great start in the right direction, but the responsibility for making proper decisions about your own health and fitness is yours. This chapter will discuss GOAL SETTING as a means of helping you realize more of your potential.

What Are Goals?

Almost anything you desire can be a goal. Buying a car, getting better grades, changing your body weight, getting stronger, getting a date with a certain person, or making the track team could be personal goals. Goals serve as a guide for what you do and give you something to work toward. Personal goals help you do your best and achieve the things you want in life.

I'M READY FOR THE CHALLENGE OF IMPROVING MYSELF, AND I'M STARTING TODAY!

Goals help you take control of your life.

In this course, the focus is on health-related fitness. Therefore, you will be encouraged to set goals in flexibility, cardiovascular fitness, muscular strength and endurance, body composition, nutrition, and weight control. You will also be encouraged to set any other health-related goals you desire.

What Is Goal Setting?

Goal setting is a process that can help you improve yourself and feel good about yourself. It is a method of getting people motivated about their own self-improvement and lifestyles. The following sections on long-term goals, short-term goals, and the steps involved in the goal-setting process will help you understand goal setting. It is not a difficult process, but it will take more than wishing. It will take some effort and commitment.

Long-term goals

Even though you may not think about it often, you probably set goals all the time. Some of your goals may take a long time to reach, perhaps years. An example of a **long-term goal** would be that you want to go to college and study to become a doctor or computer programmer. Another long-term goal could be to save money to buy a car. On the other hand, long-term goals do not have to take that long. You may want to accomplish something during this semester, such as becoming a leader in student government, and that would also be a long-term goal. None of these examples can be obtained in a short period of time. But all are achievable with the use of short-term goals.

Short-term goals

Short-term goals are goals which can be established to help you either achieve a long-term goal, or help you accomplish something in a short period of time. Short-term goals may be reached quickly, perhaps in a few days or weeks. Your short-term goals are usually very specific, while long-term goals may be more general. Examples of some short-term goals include studying hard to get a good grade on next week's algebra test or earning enough money to buy concert tickets this weekend.

Goal Setting Is Like a Ladder

Long Term Goal

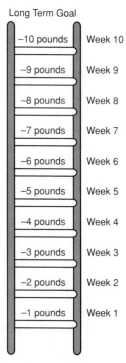

−10 pounds	Week 10
−9 pounds	Week 9
−8 pounds	Week 8
−7 pounds	Week 7
−6 pounds	Week 6
−5 pounds	Week 5
−4 pounds	Week 4
−3 pounds	Week 3
−2 pounds	Week 2
−1 pounds	Week 1

Use short-term goals to reach long-term goals.

The establishment of goals is like a ladder. Think of the top rung of a ladder as your long-term goal and the rungs leading to it as your short-term goals. Each rung (short-term goal) you climb will put you in a better position to reach your long-term goal. Notice how the ladder in the drawing shows this analogy. In this situation, the person wanted to lose ten pounds, the long-term goal shown as the top rung on the ladder. But instead of just setting a long-term goal of losing ten pounds, which could seem tough to many people, this person set ten short-term goals of losing one pound per week, shown as each of the ten rungs on the ladder. It is very important for anyone who is just beginning to set goals to start by setting short-term goals. These goals should not be that difficult to achieve, and you will feel great when you reach each one. Each one can act as motivation to encourage you to reach the next rung (short-term goal) on the ladder. By setting goals using the ladder method, you will see concrete progress and develop a sense of confidence. An increased feeling of self-confidence can fuel your psychological momentum to want to reach for higher rungs on your performance ladder.

Goal-Setting Steps

The following information on how to set personal goals will be of value to you only if you sincerely wish to make a change or changes in your lifestyle.

desire

This is the most important factor in goal setting. Wanting to improve yourself in some way is essential before you can start setting goals. *Goals are personal.* Parents, friends, or teachers cannot set goals for you. It is 100 percent up to you, although other people can help you once you have decided how you want to change. In what ways would you like to improve yourself?

belief

Wanting to make a change and doing it are two different things. You have undoubtedly known people who wanted to stop smoking or lose 15 pounds but never did it. Why do you suppose this was the case? In all probability they simply did not believe they could do it. An important point to remember always is that if you believe you cannot do something, you probably never will. On the other hand, if you really believe you can do something, you have a better chance of accomplishing it. "Want power" can become "will power." This idea is known as "the self-fulfilling prophesy."

analyze where you are now

Knowing your starting point is essential as you establish both short-term and long-term goals. For example, if you wish to lose ten pounds, it is obvious that you need to know exactly what you presently weigh. Or if your goal is to improve your diet, it would be important to get a good idea of what you currently eat over a two- or three-day period of time. Recording everything you eat and drink would provide valuable information needed to identify the steps to take for improvement to occur. You may have already taken a pre-test on your physical fitness level. If you have, you know what your starting points are for your flexibility, cardiovascular efficiency, muscular strength and endurance, and body composition.

set realistic goals

It is important for you to set goals that are realistic. A realistic goal is one you can reach. If your goals are too hard to reach, you may become discouraged and give up. If they are too easy, you may lose interest in them. Try to set goals that will stretch you somewhat and will move you out of a "comfort zone."

Accomplishing something that has stretched your "mental toughness" will make you feel good about yourself and prepare you to want to reach for higher goals. Realistic goals are those which are both reachable and challenging.

A winner is someone who has moved out of the "comfort zone." Such an individual has learned to set goals that are not too hard or too easy.

Realistic goal setting is based on your current level of physical fitness. For example, if you are only able to jog 440 yards without stopping, setting a goal of being able to jog a mile in 8 minutes in a month's time is probably unrealistic. A realistic goal for someone with this level of fitness may be to jog a mile in 12 minutes at the end of a month's time. Perhaps in a four-month period of time, the individual would be able to jog the mile in 8 minutes. In a similar way, if you can only do 1 pull-up, setting a goal of 10 additional pull-ups in a month's time may be unrealistic. On the other hand, setting a goal of 3 pull-ups in a month's time is probably realistic. Over a longer period of time, a goal of 10 pull-ups could be obtained and would be a realistic goal.

write your goals down in detail

Putting your goals down on paper helps you to clarify exactly what you want to do. When you think of something you want, it is just a wish. When it is on paper, you are moving the idea along the road to success. Writing your goals in this manner will allow you to get a clearer picture of what you want to do.

Understanding the benefits of exercise will help motivate you to exercise.

list benefits you will receive

Identifying how you will benefit from accomplishing your goals is a very important step because the benefits you list will help make your desire stronger and, therefore, make your belief in yourself stronger. For example, if you want to begin a weight-lifting program so that you will look better, what personal benefits would you list? The following would be just a few of the benefits you would hope for:

a. improved body image,

b. gain in energy,

c. improved endurance,

d. increased self-confidence and self-esteem,

e. and greater enjoyment of all types of physical activities.

The more benefits you can list for accomplishing your goal, the greater will be your desire to make it happen. Remember the discussion in Chapter 1 of all of the benefits of being physically active?

identify obstacles

If you have never set goals before, you may not recognize any blocks or obstacles to attaining your goals. On the other hand, if you have tried to do something and failed, an obstacle may be a doubt in your mind that you can really follow through and achieve your desired goal. Some obstacles may center on yourself, while other obstacles may center on your friends or your family's lifestyle. There is very little you cannot achieve in the areas of health and fitness if you have the will power and belief in yourself. *You are in the driver's seat in your own life and have the power to shape your lifestyle.*

Attack obstacles you may face in your fitness program with confidence.

identify knowledge you will need

Wanting something and knowing how to achieve it are two different things. If you want to reduce the stress in your life, you cannot wish it away. You will need to know the methods of reducing your stress before it actually happens. This need for knowledge applies to any goal you set. Your physical education teacher will be able to help you gain the knowledge and information you may need to reach your goals.

make a plan of action

After all information has been collected, making a plan is the next crucial step. Outlining a step-by-step strategy for accomplishing your goals could be called your "game plan." If your game plan is set up properly, you will experience success quickly and thus insure your continued progress toward attaining your goals.

develop time lines

While it is not easy to know exactly when you can accomplish your fitness goals, you may be able to get a pretty good idea, particularly if you seek advice from your physical education teacher. Setting **time lines** (times when something will be completed) is a simple and effective method to organize and plot your course to a major goal. Think of a fitness goal you would like to achieve this semester. For example, suppose you want to jog for 30 minutes without stopping by the end of the semester. The drawing shows how this could be done with time lines. Notice that while a time line does not provide you with the strategies to reach your goal, it does set some deadlines for you to have made progress toward your goal.

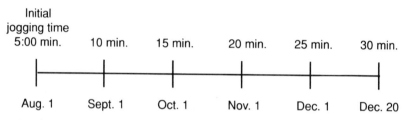

| Initial jogging time 5:00 min. | 10 min. | 15 min. | 20 min. | 25 min. | 30 min. |
| Aug. 1 | Sept. 1 | Oct. 1 | Nov. 1 | Dec. 1 | Dec. 20 |

A time line helps you to pace your efforts toward reaching your goal.

Writing out your goals and putting them on a time line makes them easier to accomplish. Using time lines:

a. gives you a better sense of control, organization, and direction,

b. promotes greater commitment to your goals,

c. helps relieve worry and confusion, especially as your individual deadlines approach,

d. helps you pace your efforts,

e. and creates a sense of urgency to reach goals.

monitor your progress

Any goal setting or planning should be accompanied by continuous monitoring to determine whether your goals are still reasonable. You may find that you need to readjust your short-term goals or even your long-term goals. A good monitoring process will keep you from wasting time or losing interest in your goals. The worst thing that can happen is that you may lose the belief that you can stick to your program. That would be very self-defeating. You can also get feedback from your parents, physical education teachers, or supportive friends.

never give up

Back your plan with a solid determination that you will never give up. If you are just beginning to set goals, it could be very easy to give up. Do not be led off track, either by yourself or by others. Avoid sharing your goals with anyone who is "not in your corner." *Be determined to take control of your lifestyle.* Such determination will mean a lot to you.

Seeing progress can help to keep you from losing interest in your goals.

Goal Setting in Action

The following case study is an example of a course of action one high school student undertook to reach her goals.

Jodi was a 15-year-old tenth grader who did not feel comfortable in sports activities. Like most teenagers, she was concerned about looking as good as possible and feeling good about herself. Jodi was 5 feet 4 inches tall and weighed 128 pounds. When she took the physical fitness test at the beginning of the semester, she scored at the 25th percentile level in the mile run (12:21), and her percentage of body fat was much higher than she wanted. Jodi did not like scoring so low in the mile run or having such a high percentage of body fat. The real problem she had with her weight was the fact that some of her clothes were not fitting as well as they had just a few months earlier.

As a result of a discussion on goal setting in class, she made up her mind to lose 10 pounds, which would help reduce her percentage of body fat. She also decided she wanted to be able to run the mile at least 2 minutes and fifteen seconds faster, which would raise her to the 50th percentile level (10:15) for her age. Jodi wanted to do this in nine weeks, by the time for her next physical fitness test.

After writing down her goals, Jodi made the following list of the ways she would benefit from accomplishing these two goals:

a. Her appearance would be improved.

b. She would be less self conscious with her friends.

c. She would feel good about herself because she had accomplished a difficult task.

d. She would be more physically fit and confident in physical education class.

e. She would be more willing to "dress out" for physical education.

f. She could wear clothes at least one size smaller.

g. She would feel more confident to tackle other challenges in her life.

goal one

Jodi knew that in order to reach her long-term goals, she would have to set several short-term goals in both areas if she wanted to be successful. She developed the following plan to meet her goals:

Jodi recognized that her diet contained too much junk food, but she did not know how much. Her first step was to monitor and record everything she ate and drank for three days. This provided her with a baseline of information about the amount and kinds of foods she was eating. An analysis of her food intake revealed that she ate very few fruits and vegetables, frequently stopped at fast-food restaurants, and ate too much junk food every day.

Based on her findings and information obtained in the chapter on nutrition, she resolved to:

a. eat at fast-food restaurants no more than twice a week and to make good choices when she did,

b. reduce the amount of junk food she would eat and replace it with more nutritious snacks,

c. and eat at least two fruits and vegetables every day.

Jodi knew these three changes in her nutritional behavior would not be easy, but she was tired of being "a little overweight."

goal two

In order to reduce her mile-run time by 2 minutes and fifteen seconds, Jodi knew the only answer was not only to run more often, but also to be more active overall. She developed the following plan to meet this long-term goal:

a. buy a pair of comfortable jogging shoes which would provide good arch support,

b. walk/jog three times a week at school for 15 minutes without worrying about distance traveled during the next four weeks,

c. cycle or play tennis with one of her parents or a friend at least twice a week,

d. jog continuously for 15 minutes by the end of the 5th week,

e. reduce her time for the mile run at least one minute (11:20) by the end of the 5th week,

f. increase her three training runs at school to 20 minutes duration during the 6th, 7th, and 8th weeks,

g. and retake the test for the mile run and achieve the 50th percentile level by the end of the 9th week.

Throughout the nine weeks, Jodi planned to weigh herself at the same time each Friday with the anticipation of losing from one to one-and-a-half pounds each week. To help her accomplish her goals, she decided to keep a personal log of her efforts in both areas. She thought that recording her feelings and activities throughout the nine weeks would be motivational and help her maintain her momentum. She also planned to share her log with her physical education teacher and close friends whom she knew would give her feedback and encouragement.

When she reached the end of the nine-week time period and achieved her goals, she planned to celebrate by buying herself a new outfit. Jodi believed very strongly that she would reach her goals.

Do you think Jodi was successful in reaching her goals? What were the steps she took? She certainly had all of the elements necessary to be successful since she:

a. had both the desire to improve and a belief that she could do it,

b. assessed herself and knew where she was in both of her goal areas,

c. identified how she would benefit from reaching her goals,

d. set a very specific plan with specific time lines as to when she hoped to accomplish certain things,

e. monitored her progress and planned to get the help of her physical education teacher to give her feedback and direction,

f. and believed in herself and did not give up.

Jodi had concerns similar to those of a lot of young people. She not only wanted to look and feel as good as possible, but also to perform as well as she could. If you develop a plan tailored to meet your needs, there is no question that you will become a successful goal setter.

Summary

The teen years can be a difficult time as well as a positive adventure. Learning to take control of more aspects of your life through good decision making is very rewarding. Becoming an effective goal setter will be a natural positive force in your life. If done properly, the process will give you added confidence and a stronger belief in yourself as you take more control of various aspects of your life.

The steps in goal setting are to:

Goal setting is a lot like golf. It's the follow through that counts.

1. have the desire to improve,

2. believe that you will be successful,

3. analyze where you are right now,

4. set realistic goals,

5. write down both your long- and short-term goals in detail,

6. list benefits you will receive by reaching your goals,

7. identify the obstacles that may be in your way,

8. identify the knowledge you may need to reach your goals,

9. make a plan of action to reach your goals,

10. develop time lines for both short-term and long-term goals,

11. monitor your progress closely with a personal log,

12. and never give up.

By keeping your goals *appropriate, attainable,* and as *specific* as possible, you will gain momentum to continue on to the next challenge. Remember that goal setting and planning are ongoing processes; therefore, feel free to modify and adapt your plans so that they remain appropriate for you. Do not be upset with yourself if you deviate from your program on a given day. That is only human nature. Goal setting may not be easy at first, but it will become smoother as you persist. Goal setting can become an exciting process in any aspect of your life. *Do not hold back; give it your best shot.*

Study Questions

True–false

The following is a list of some things that you might do as you work toward your goals. Circle "T" if the statement describes something that will help you achieve your goals. Circle "F" if it describes something that will *not* help you.

T F 1. Avoid setting time lines.

T F 2. Use your resources wisely.

T F 3. Postpone setting long-term goals.

T F 4. List benefits you will receive.

T F 5. Ask parents or teachers to set goals for you.

T F 6. Write your goals down in detail.

T F 7. Do not worry about obstacles you may face.

T F 8. Identify how you will benefit from accomplishing your goal.

T F 9. Never readjust your goals.

T F 10. Never give up.

Discussion

11. What are two things that make your life "topsy-turvy?"

12. What goals could you set that would made these things less stressful if the goals were accomplished?

13. How are "desire" and "belief in oneself" important in accomplishing goals?

14. What are the steps necessary for successful goal setting?

15. Identify five goals that you would like to accomplish this year.

Chapter Objectives

As you read this chapter, look for answers to these key questions:

- What should you consider when beginning an exercise program?

- What considerations should be made regarding clothing for an exercise program?

- What precautions should be taken when exercising in hot weather? Cold weather?

- What are the symptoms of heat exhaustion and heat stroke?

- What other safety factors should you consider when you exercise?

- How do you maintain a proper fluid balance during physical activity?

- What are the steps in warming-up and cooling-down?

- What injuries might you encounter when beginning an exercise program?

When you have completed this chapter, you should understand the meaning of these vocabulary terms:

hyperthermia	warm-up
heat cramps	cool-down
heat exhaustion	shin splint
heat stroke	diaphragm
hypothermia	stitch-in-the-side

Getting Started

Exercise is to the body as reading is to the mind.

G. Legman

The purpose of this chapter is to help you get a positive start in your personal fitness program. Chapter 14 is specifically designed to help you establish your own personal fitness program. However, it is important that you get started as soon as possible if you have things you would like to improve in your lifestyle. The next chapter on Principles of Training is also related to starting a program since it covers such factors as how hard, how often, and how long people should exercise. There are a number of other important guidelines to keep in mind as you begin your program, and these are the focus of this chapter.

Medical exam

If you are in good health and have not been ill, you will not need to have a medical exam before beginning a personal fitness program. It is recommended that anyone who has experienced ill health or is over thirty years of age should have a medical exam before beginning a personal fitness program. This is especially important if a person has not been physically active. The medical exam should include what is known as an exercise stress test. During this test, the heart's response to exercise is monitored closely by a physician.

Fitness evaluation

You should evaluate your level of physical fitness prior to beginning a personal fitness program. This will allow you to set realistic goals and to determine your progress over a period of time. Recall that the methods of assessment were discussed in Chapter 2. Assessment should cover all health-related components of physical fitness, including flexibility, cardiovascular fitness, muscular strength and endurance, and body composition.

Your current level of physical fitness will determine how and where you should begin exercising, which activities to choose, and whether you want to develop a program that will maintain or improve your current level of physical fitness. Once you have determined your level of fitness, you will be ready to set realistic and challenging goals for your personal fitness program. In addition, the information on your current level of physical fitness will help you determine improvement with periodic reevaluations.

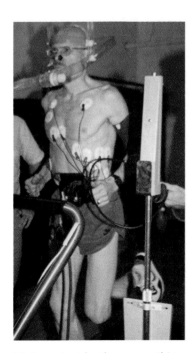

It is important for those over thirty years of age to have a medical exam and an exercise stress test.

Goal setting

The previous chapter on Goal Setting is a key component in establishing a personal fitness program. When setting goals for your personal fitness program, you are really setting lifestyle goals. Your goals should include both long- and short-term goals, be realistic, and serve as motivators. Set specific goals that are both attainable and challenging for each health-related component of physical fitness. Evaluate your short-term goals periodically, modifying them as necessary. Your long-term goals may remain the same. Concentrate on improving your lifestyle over a long period of time. Celebrate the fact that you are on a personal trip to becoming a greater person.

What You Wear Can Make a Difference

Your program and the weather basically determine what you should wear. The general rule is to have good shoes, clean socks that fit, appropriate undergarments, and loose-fitting clothing. Keep in mind that your body's cooling process requires that air pass over the skin to evaporate sweat. Clothing must allow this evaporative process to take place.

Shoes

Sound footwear is the major requirement for effective care and protection of your feet. Shoes should be designed well, constructed from the best possible materials, and fit well. Purchasing quality athletic shoes is a wise investment. Note in the drawing the major features to look for when buying shoes for walking or jogging. When buying athletic shoes, take time to examine the shoes carefully and answer these questions. Do they have good arch supports? Do they have wedge

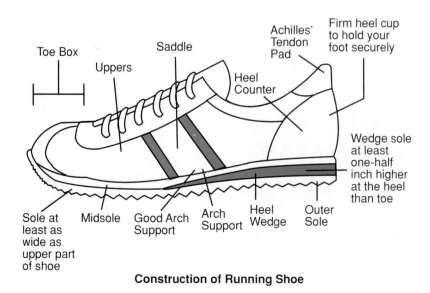

Construction of Running Shoe

soles at least one-half inch higher at the heel than at the toe? Are the soles at least as wide as the upper part of the shoes? Do they have firm heel cups to hold your feet securely? Do they have soft, well cushioned inner soles? Are there any rough seams or edges inside the shoes that may cause blisters? Finally, are they the correct size in terms of both width and length? Once you have purchased it, keep your footwear clean and in good repair.

Be a smart consumer when buying shoes. Get advice from a knowledgeable person. Remember, you do not always have to pay a lot of money for quality.

Socks

When you try on athletic shoes, be sure to wear the same type of socks as you will be wearing when you participate in your fitness activity. A small factor such as this may change the fit of the shoes slightly and cause them to feel uncomfortable when you exercise. Socks prevent direct friction of the skin against the shoes, which may cause blisters. In general, it is better to wear two pairs of socks, since this will provide more comfort and protection against blisters. Regardless of whether you are wearing one or two pairs of socks, be sure your socks are clean and fit properly. You also should make sure there are no wrinkles or folds in your socks before putting on your shoes.

Shirts

A regular T-shirt is very appropriate for most activities. Such shirts are predominantly cotton, which provides excellent absorbency and allows the body to breathe. In addition, they are comfortable, durable, easy to wash, and inexpensive. Nylon shirts make cooling more difficult because this material traps sweat, thereby not allowing body heat to be transferred to the air. Common sense tells you never to wear dark-colored shirts at night because of safety considerations and to wear a white shirt in hot weather because white best reflects the sun's rays.

Dress as lightly as possible in hot weather.

Shorts

The main concern in choosing shorts is that they should not be too tight around the thighs. A tight fit may rub and chafe the body. One way to reduce irritation and chafing is to rub petroleum jelly on your legs where your shorts contact the skin.

Exercising in Hot Weather

Exercise with caution in a hot environment.

The maintenance of your body's internal temperature is very important. When you exercise, blood flow is concentrated in the working muscles, causing a heat buildup. This is caused by your blood transferring internal heat from your working muscles to the skin, where it is given off to the outside air. You rely on the air's absorption of heat from your skin surface to keep your body temperature from climbing too high.

A warm environment with high humidity makes this transfer of heat very difficult. Although sweating is likely to occur, the sweat you produce fails to evaporate because the air is full of moisture, and there is no place for the liquid sweat to go. This causes less body heat to be transferred to the air. Your body temperature will continue to rise and may create a fluid deficiency in your body if you keep exercising.

A reduction of body fluids or an increase in body temperature, called **hyperthermia,** can create conditions that are uncomfortable and even life threatening. It is, therefore, very important for those who exercise in warm or hot environments to learn the symptoms, treatment, and preventive measures for the following heat-related body conditions.

Heat cramps are the least serious heat-related problem. Certain muscles (frequently the calf muscle) will contract involuntarily and will cause pain. If this happens to you, stop the activity, apply direct pressure, rest, and drink plenty of water.

Heat exhaustion is a condition characterized by profuse sweating accompanied by dizziness and extreme weakness. You should stop physical activity and immediately try to cool the body. Take fluids immediately and continuously until the symptoms have passed. Moving to a shaded area and applying wet towels will also help.

Heat stroke is a true medical emergency. This condition is characterized by hot, dry skin and a rising body temperature which may reach 106 degrees. On occasion, unconsciousness may follow. Seek medical assistance immediately. Every attempt must be made to cool the body with an ice massage, cool water immersion, or by any other means.

Heat illnesses, symptoms, and treatment. The following table presents an outline of heat illnesses. Everyone should be familiar with these conditions and how to protect against them.

	If you have any of the symptoms below, you may be developing a heat injury.		Be prepared to take appropriate actions.	
Heat Cramps	• Thirst • Chills • Clammy skin	• Throbbing heart beat • Nausea	You should: • Drink ½ cup of water every 10–15 minutes	• During breaks, move to shade and remove as much clothing as possible
Heat Exhaustion	• Profuse sweating • Dizziness • Headache • Shortness of breath	• Weak, rapid pulse • Lack of saliva • Extreme fatigue	You should: • Stop exercise and move to a cool environment • Drink 2 cups of water for every pound lost	• Take off wet clothing and sit on a chair in a cold shower • Place an ice bag on your head
Heat Stroke	• Lack of sweat • Dry, hot skin • Lack of urine • Hallucinations • Swollen tongue • Deafness	• Visual disturbances • Aggression • Unsteady walking • Excessively high body temperature	You should: • Call for emergency medical treatment • Until help arrives, place ice bags on back and front of head	• Remove clothing and rub alcohol over most of the body • Sit on chair in cold shower

Preventive measures for heat illness

There are several important points to remember when exercising in a hot or humid environment:

1. Light-weight and perforated clothing with adequate exposure of arms and legs promote the escape of heat from the skin surfaces. Lighter colors are preferred since they reflect rather than absorb the sun's rays.

2. Rubberized suits do not promote permanent weight reduction, as many people believe. Such suits can be very dangerous because they cause an elevation of the internal body temperature.

3. Drink fluids before, during, and following your exercise sessions. Do so whether you are thirsty or not. Interestingly enough, when your body is in some stage of dehydration, thirst is not always a good indicator of your body's need for fluids. You should drink two quarts of water each day even if you are not participating in a physical fitness program.

4. Wear a light-weight and light-colored cap to shade your head from the sun.

5. The use of salt tablets is not recommended. Excessive salt tends to irritate the stomach lining and has also been indicated as a risk factor in high blood pressure.

6. On extremely hot and humid days, it is recommended that you confine your exercise to a water environment and/or exercise during the early or later portions of the day when the heat is less intense.

Drink water before, during, and after exercising.

Remember, if you are exercising with a friend whose skin becomes flushed and hot, whose breathing becomes difficult, or who appears incoherent, **he or she needs immediate medical help.** Follow the above safety guidelines even in cooler weather since the body can also have difficulty cooling itself when the weather is not hot.

Exercising in cold weather

Exposure to severe, winter-like conditions, including below-freezing temperatures, icy winds, and precipitation, can also create serious problems for you. These conditions can result in an excessive decline in body temperature called **hypothermia,** as well as cause frostbite (the crystallization and eventual destruction of skin and underlying tissues) to your limbs and exposed portions of your face. Even if you are fit, be sure to increase your warm-up time and start your exercise slowly with a more gradual energy output than normal. Be aware of the fact that the colder you are, the lower your potential level of operational effectiveness.

Dress in layers and cover your head and hands to prevent heat loss during cold weather.

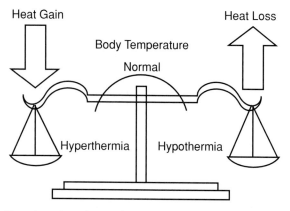

Hypothermia or heat exhaustion may occur if the body is unable to maintain equilibrium between heat loss and heat gain.

If you do perform such cold weather activities as jogging, ice skating, skiing, or sled riding, you can offset the effects of your exposure to very cold temperatures and winds by taking the following precautions:

1. Use thermal underwear and outer wear.

2. Wear gloves, face mask, and hat.

3. Wear several layers of light clothing. These are more protective and less cumbersome than one heavy, bulky layer and can be discarded more readily if no longer needed.

4. Do not overdress, since too much clothing can cause you to perspire excessively, making your clothes wet. Damp clothing can both be uncomfortable and cause you to feel chilled.

5. Wear water-resistant outer garments when exposed to snow or rain in addition to cold. Hypothermia tends to occur more rapidly when clothing is wet (even in temperatures above freezing). Wet clothing provides little insulation and actually accelerates the loss of internal body heat.

Additional Safety Precautions

Have you been under the weather?

If you are not feeling well, you should stop exercising until you feel better. Whenever there is a chance that physical activity may aggravate a minor illness, infection, or injury, you should quit exercising until you are feeling better. If you are recovering from an illness, begin physical activity at a lower level than that at which you were exercising before your illness.

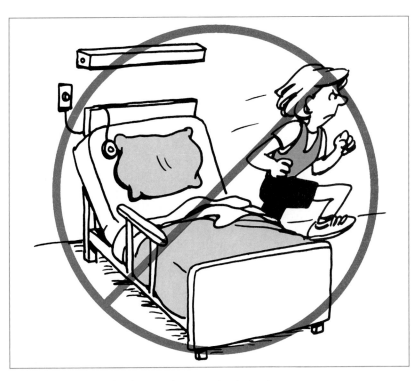

If you have been under the weather, start back slowly.

Should you exercise after a big meal?

The answer to this question centers on the definition of a big meal. If you have just eaten a big Thanksgiving dinner, you should decrease or suspend vigorous physical activity for two or three hours. However, a leisurely walk with family or friends after the meal does not interfere with digestive processes. School lunches are not considered big meals; therefore, you do not have to worry about how much you eat prior to physical activity. Whenever you are going to participate in some very vigorous sports activity, it makes sense to eat a light meal, so you will not only be able to perform more efficiently, but you will also feel better.

It has been found that exercising before a meal will reduce your appetite. If you want to lose weight, exercising before a meal may be the best time for you to participate in your personal fitness program.

Air pollution

If you live near a big city, you may see people exercising near heavily traveled highways or other areas where there is a high degree of air pollution. If at all possible, find another area, such as a park, in which to exercise. The upper portion of your air passages has an outstanding filtering system for most of the larger particles. On the other hand, it

If possible, exercise in less polluted areas.

has been shown that very small particles are not filtered out of the air and can end up in your lungs. The benefits of exercise do tend to overshadow the dangers, but exercising during smog alerts common to some areas should be avoided.

Dogs

Dogs can pose a problem for walkers, joggers, and cyclists. While their bark is usually more serious than their bite, the exceptions can be very hazardous. Dogs tend to be very protective of "their" territory, so avoiding them makes sense.

Personal safety

If possible, exercise with another person or with a group. Many people find it easier to stick with an exercise program if they exercise with friends, and there is also added safety in numbers. People can sometimes be far more dangerous than dogs. Females, in particular, must be alert to dangerous situations. Exercising with others, staying away from unpopulated areas, eliminating outdoor, nighttime exercise, and staying alert can help avoid danger.

Warming Up

The **warm-up** is a 10- to 15-minute period during which you prepare your body for vigorous exercise. Some people want instant success and forego the warm-up. Such impatience invites pain and injury. A warm-up is very helpful from both a physical and mental standpoint and may determine whether or not you continue to participate in the activity selected.

Start with a brisk walk or slow jog, then stop and do 7–10 minutes of stretching exercises.

Benefits of warming up

It makes sense that warm muscles can be safely stretched to greater ranges of motion than cold muscles. Thus, the more flexible you become, the more you can minimize injuries that might be sustained during a slip or stumble. In addition, a loose and flexible body can better react to and absorb sudden falls and awkward positions that are potential aspects of vigorous exercise. In summary, a warm-up will not bring about early fatigue or hinder performance, but it will prepare the body for activity and help prevent injury. You will find that a warm-up will energize you and make exercising more fun.

Engaging in a proper warm-up period before you exercise:

1. helps you mentally focus your effort and makes you feel like moving.

2. increases your heart rate and the blood supply to your muscles, thus preparing your cardiovascular and muscular systems for the workout.

3. generates heat in the muscle and joint tissues, which makes them more flexible and resistant to injury.

How to warm up

A warm-up usually includes a general and a specific component. The *general component* has three stages. The first stage includes some type of large muscle activity such as running in place or slow jogging. This activity is designed to raise the heart rate slowly while increasing muscle temperature. The second stage involves static stretching. Muscles should be stretched slowly for 15 to 30 seconds and progressively to the point of discomfort, not pain.

The *specific component* of warming-up involves participation in the activity to be performed or a related activity. For example, if you are jogging, you might jog the first half mile of the workout at a leisurely pace, slowly increasing to the desired speed. In this way, your body is allowed to gradually adapt to the specific stress to be imposed upon it. Some people go through the motions of the sport when they warm up. If you are going to play tennis for example, you will want to warm up your shoulder and arm muscles. You might want to volley the ball back and forth across the net with your partner or practice a few serves before starting the game.

There is a misconception that warm-ups should only be done when you engage in aerobic activities. Warming up is important in all activities. The concepts of general and specific warm-up apply to biking, jogging, racquetball, rope jumping, swimming, tennis, weight lifting, and all other activities.

The warm-up must become a habit. Many people do not warm up properly and get away without any apparent problems. To be on the safe side, why not do it?

Cooling Down

The **cool-down** is a 10- to 15-minute period of mild exercise that follows your training session and allows your body and heart rate to return to their resting states slowly. Cooling down from exercise is as important as warming up. Just as your body was allowed to speed up gradually, it must also be allowed to slow down gradually.

Benefits of cooling down

The explanation for a cool-down period following a rigorous workout is not difficult to understand. Blood returns to the heart through a system of vessels called veins. The muscles squeeze the veins and thus push the blood toward the heart. If you stop exercising suddenly, the return blood flow through the veins is reduced. When this happens, the blood return to the heart will drop quickly and may cause the blood to pool in your legs. This will result in less oxygen going to other body parts, such as the head.

Engaging in a proper cool-down period after you exercise:

1. helps to prevent blood from pooling in the muscles you were using. Without a cool-down, less blood reaches your heart, and you may feel light-headed.
2. prevents tightened muscles from becoming sore.

How to cool down

Your cool-down should be as long as, or even slightly longer than, your warm-up. The first phase of cooling down should consist of walking or some other light activity to prevent blood from pooling in the muscles that were used. Your cool-down period should continue until your heart rate is around 100 beats per minute.

For your cool-down, repeat some of the same stretching exercises you performed during the warm-up.

The second phase of a cool-down should focus upon the same stretching exercises that were used during the warm-up period. You will probably note that stretching is easier after exercising due to the increase in muscle temperature. Stretching at this time loosens tightened muscles and helps prevent muscle soreness.

Bent-leg sit-ups may be added to the cool-down routine. Strong abdominal muscles are a postural aid because they provide support for the upper torso. Remember, many researchers and physical education teachers believe the cool-down is as important or more important than the warm-up.

Common Injuries

If you start your program sensibly and in a gradual manner, the likelihood of incurring any injuries is greatly reduced. However, it is important that you are able to recognize the symptoms of some of the more common injuries that people who are involved in physical activity encounter.

Muscle soreness

Muscle soreness is a very common problem which usually appears within the first 12 to 24 hours following exertion. In almost all cases, it is the result of starting a program that is too strenuous at the beginning. The discomfort is thought to be due to chemical changes in the muscles and microscopic tears in the muscle fibers and connective tissues. The soreness may be very noticeable and may persist for one to two days. It does diminish gradually. Light massage, easy static stretching, and mild exercise may also be of value in reducing the discomfort. The key point is that nearly all of this pain can be eliminated simply by starting your program in a cautious manner.

Blisters

A blister is a localized problem which is the result of friction creating heat, tissue damage, and fluid accumulation between the layers of skin in an attempt to prevent further tissue damage. The fluid may be clear or "bloody," creating a "blood blister."

Once a blister has formed, it can be extremely painful. If the blister has broken, it must be treated as if it were an open wound. After the wound is cleansed, a sterile dressing should be applied. If the blister is unbroken, then two approaches may be considered. First, it may be protected from pressure by applying appropriate gauze padding over the blister. Another way of protecting the blister is to place a "doughnut" shaped piece of foam over it. A second method of treating a blister is to puncture its side with a sterilized needle to release the accumulated fluid. Then it must be treated with an antiseptic and covered tightly. The dressing must be kept clean to reduce the chances of infection. Never remove the layer of skin which covers a blister unless it has been torn loose. The skin covering will aid in protecting the sensitive underlying and newly forming layer of skin.

Shin splints

A **shin splint** is an inflammation of the membrane on the front of the bones in the lower leg. A shin splint is an over-use syndrome (you did too much too quickly) which will typically develop in poorly conditioned individuals in the beginning of their programs. Hard surfaces, improper shoes, running on the balls of your feet, and overdoing it are the primary reasons for developing shin splints. Treatment consists of rest, ice packs, taping the sore area, and elevation.

Stitch-in-the-side

A **stitch-in-the-side** may develop in individuals who are beginning a jogging program. It is a rather sharp pain in the side, just under the ribs. While the cause is unknown, there are a number of theories. Some think it is caused by faulty breathing, reduced blood flow to the area, or accumulation of lactic acid in and around the **diaphragm**—a large muscle in your upper abdomen. If you experience this pain, apply pressure to the affected area, stretch to the opposite side and breathe deeply. Once in good physical condition, you will rarely experience this type of pain.

Direct pressure to the affected area may give you some relief from a "stitch-in-the-side."

Sprained ankle

Sprains are injuries to ligaments surrounding a joint or to the capsule-like sac that surrounds a joint. Although a severe sprain may not be distinguishable from a more serious fracture except by X ray, you should stop the activity, apply ice, elevate the injured part, and immobilize the ankle.

Summary

It is very important when beginning a personal fitness program to follow certain guidelines. The first step is to clearly outline what you want to do and then begin in low gear. Many people begin too quickly and become injured. Understanding weather conditions and heat-related illnesses which may occur when exercising outside is of extreme importance. In hot weather, people may exercise too hard and lose too much water from their bodies by sweating. Drinking plenty of water before, during, and after exercise is a guideline you should always remember. Warming the body up before exercise and cooling it down properly after exercise are also very important habits for being successful in your quest for self improvement.

Success is the name of the game. There is nothing like self-improvement to offset a bored attitude toward your program. Knowing where you started and the progress you have made are key factors toward success.

The last guideline is to be patient. Seeing big changes in your performance may take a few weeks. If your body is out of shape, remember that it took quite a long time for it to get that way. It will therefore take you more than a few days to get back into shape. On the other hand, as soon as you get started on your program, you can expect to feel good about yourself since you will be following a positive game plan to improve your lifestyle by looking and feeling as good as possible.

Study Questions

True–false

Circle "T" for all correct statements and "F" for all incorrect ones.

T F 1. Selecting proper shoes is the most important consideration when choosing your exercise wardrobe.

T F 2. The color of clothing does not make any difference when you are exercising in hot weather.

T F 3. It is important that you evaluate your level of fitness prior to beginning a personal fitness program.

T F 4. Microscopic tears in muscle fibers and connective tissue are one cause of muscle soreness after you exercise.

T F 5. Dressing in layers during cold weather is an exercise myth.

T F 6. On a day with high humidity, your body is easily cooled by evaporation because you sweat more.

T F 7. It is best to limit fluid intake to people who are sweating profusely because the water may cause stomach cramps.

T   F   8. Shin splints are typically caused by overuse of poorly conditioned muscles.

T   F   9. A common treatment for blisters is to place a "doughnut" shaped piece of foam over the blister.

T   F   10. The exact cause of a "stitch-in-the-side" is not known.

Discussion

11. Your aunt is starting to take an aerobics class at a local health spa and has been advised to wear appropriate shoes. She does not know anything about athletic shoes and asks you about this matter. What would you tell her about selecting the proper shoes?

12. You live in Florida and a cousin from Cleveland comes to visit you in July. Your cousin has not been very active, but he wants to get started on a personal fitness program. He wants to exercise in the afternoon since he does not get up very early in the morning. What are some important guidelines you should give him? What should he wear?

13. Design a general and specific warm-up for an activity you engage in.

14. What is the purpose of cooling down after exercising?

15. Why do so many people complain about muscle soreness the day after a vigorous physical workout?

Chapter Objectives

As you read this chapter, look for answers to these key questions:

- How does the principle of overload increase your fitness level?
- In what three ways is overload accomplished?
- Why is it important for you to progress at a safe rate in your exercise program?
- What principle would you apply if you wished to improve a specific muscle?

When you have completed this chapter, you should understand the meaning of these vocabulary terms:

principle of overload
F.I.T.
frequency
intensity
time
principle of progression
principle of specificity

Efficient and Safe Training

You will only get out of training what you put into it.

In order to look good, feel good, and enjoy a healthy lifestyle, it is essential that you engage in regular physical activity. However, before you enter into a training program, review the considerations covered in Chapter 4. You must consider your previous involvement in physical activity, present fitness level, present health, and past medical history.

To operate efficiently and avoid injury, you must follow a carefully planned and deliberate training program. There are three basic training principles to be followed in developing your program: overload, progression, and specificity.

Principle of Overload

In general terms, the various systems of the body will become stronger and function better if increased demands (overload) are placed upon them. While it is important to overload your body so improvement may occur, the stress should not be so severe that your body would be unable to adjust. For example, your body would not be able to adapt to an overload of lifting 300 pounds on your first attempt to increase muscular strength. Not only would you be unsuccessful and not enjoy the exercise session, but you might also cause harm to your body.

As previously mentioned, physical fitness is a personal matter. The amount of overload needed varies with each individual. Some of your friends may have to work more on flexibility, whereas you may have to work harder on muscular endurance. The amount of overload needed by different individuals can easily be seen when comparing a young person and an older person. For example, if your grandmother has been inactive, she may find a fast walk stressful, while you may have to jog for two miles to achieve an overload.

One of the first known examples of the **overload principle** is traced back to the legendary Milo of Crotona. This famous athlete increased his strength by lifting a small calf several times a week. As the calf grew heavier and heavier, Milo's muscles became stronger, allowing him to lift more and more weight. Milo's use of the overload principle made him the only person in his village to have the strength to lift a full-size bull.

Milo of Crotona—legendary use of overload principle to develop strength

FIT = frequency/intensity/time

The principle of overload may be accomplished by increasing one of three variables:

Frequency (how often you exercise)
Intensity (how hard you exercise)
Time (how long you exercise)

The first letter of these three words spell fit. **FIT** can be used as a reminder of the three ways to achieve overload in your physical fitness program.

Frequency

Frequency refers to the fact that exercise must be performed regularly if you are to reach and maintain an adequate level of physical fitness. Ideally, your exercise program will be a daily habit, just as brushing your teeth is. You can imagine the effects of not brushing your teeth on a regular basis. Similarly, there is a connection between how frequently you exercise and your outward appearance (``looking good'') and how healthy you are (``feeling good''). Limiting your exercises to weekend recreational activity would be like brushing your teeth only on these days. Exercising three days a week is the minimum frequency (how often you exercise) and will increase your level of fitness if the time (how long you exercise) is increased.

How often you exercise depends on your goals. If you want the cardiorespiratory benefits of aerobic exercise, you should exercise at least three times a week. Exercising five times a week, however, is more effective. If you want to lose weight, most experts recommend exercising moderately six days a week. Weight training requires time for the muscles to rest and recover. Therefore, a specific muscle should not be overloaded more than every other day for muscular strength or endurance training.

FIT = FREQUENCY + INTENSITY + TIME

Sun.	Mon.	Tue.	Wed.	Thur.	Fri.	Sat.
	1	2	3	4	5	6
7	8	9	10	11	12	13
14	15	16	17	18	19	20
21	22	23	24	25	26	27
28	29	30	31			

- At least 3 times per week

- 50-85% maximal heart rate reserve

- 20 minutes to 60 minutes duration of time recommended

FIT can be used to remember the methods to increase overload.

Intensity

The **intensity** of all exercises should be hard enough to demand more effort than usual. How much harder you must work is a critical question, since over-strenuous exercises may cause injury, while not training hard enough will result in little or no improvement. If you have been playing soccer on a regular basis, jogging one mile twice a week would not be a hard enough workout to improve cardiovascular fitness.

How hard should you exercise to develop an acceptable level of fitness? It depends upon the fitness component (cardiovascular, strength, endurance, or flexibility) and your present level of fitness. To improve your cardiovascular fitness, you make your heart work harder than it normally does. The intensity of a workout is indicated by the number of times per minute your heart beats during your activity. The faster your heart rate, the more intense the exercise. Making your heart work harder by running faster would be one application of intensity to improve cardiovascular fitness. A number of activities besides running will develop cardiovascular fitness. Swimming, bicycling, and aerobic dance are a few such examples. For muscular strength and endurance you work harder, or increase intensity, by lifting more weight. To increase intensity for flexibility improvement, you work harder by stretching the muscle beyond its normal length.

Time

Time relates to how long you exercise. How many minutes do you jog (cardiovascular), lift weights (muscular strength and endurance), or perform stretching exercises (flexibility)? In order to be effective, a training session must be maintained for a certain length of time. For example, to develop cardiovascular fitness you would need to maintain the activity for twenty to sixty minutes.

Research shows that as time is increased, intensity will decrease. This means that a beginner can spread the training session over a longer period of time at an easier pace. Rather than biking four miles in fifteen minutes, cover the same distance in twenty minutes, at an easier pace. Anyone who is excessively overweight may not only need to walk instead of jog (reduce intensity level), but also limit their workout to a fifteen- or twenty-minute session and gradually work up to a longer period of time.

Skipping a workout session to permit the body to rest is acceptable and may help prevent injuries. However, be careful not to allow a one day lay-off turn into two, then into three, and so on until you stop exercising all together.

Principle of Progression

As you work harder (overload), your body adapts. Because your body becomes accustomed to this workload, you must progressively increase the amount of work for improvement to occur. If you progressively increase the load, like Milo of Crotona, you will improve fitness and prevent injuries. For example, cardiovascular fitness would be improved if you began a training program that involved running one mile a day in eight minutes over the next several weeks. However, if you continued to run the same distance in the same amount of time after your body had adapted to this workload, cardiovascular improvement would stop. To continue improving, you would have to increase your intensity by running your mile in seven minutes or increase distance to one and a half miles. This would again put the overload principle into effect. Over a period of time, additional overload would have to be added.

It is very important that you know when it is safe to progress. Think of the **principle of progression** as the schedule for the application of overload. You want to slowly and progressively apply stress to the body only when it is needed and not before. If your exercise level is too intense or your exercise session is too long, you may feel unusually tired during the session or even for a few hours after it. This is a signal that you have placed too much overload on your body. Other signs of overexertion include nausea or vomiting during or after a workout and muscle or joint aches and pains that do not go away quickly. If you experience any of these symptoms, you need to reduce your exercise intensity and time. This is why it is important to evaluate the health-related components of physical fitness and to record daily

TRAIN — DON'T STRAIN

Gradually increase overload.

achievements. With such measurements, records of progress, and knowledge of training principles, you will know when it is safe to progress and increase your overload.

Principle of Specificity

The **principle of specificity** means you must do specific exercises to improve specific components of physical fitness in specific body parts. For example, flexibility exercises will increase flexibility, but will not necessarily improve cardiovascular fitness. Stretching your legs will not increase flexibility in your arms. Another example is when a person who has trained for a specific sport such as gymnastics, attempts to play basketball and quickly becomes fatigued. Each physical activity requires specific demands, and doing the activity is the best way to train for it.

WHAT DO YOU MEAN, I HAVE LOW CARDIOVASCULAR FITNESS?

You must do specific exercises to improve cardiovascular fitness.

Summary

Three basic training principles (overload, progression, and specificity) must be observed when you design an exercise program. An overload must be added beyond what is normally placed on the body in daily activity. You can place overload on the body by increasing one or more of the overload variables: **frequency** (how often you work), **intensity** (how hard you work), or **time** (how long you work). A good way of remembering the three overload variables is to think of the word FIT (Frequency, Intensity, Time).

Body systems adapt to the specific stresses placed upon them. As your body adapts, you must progressively increase the overload to improve your level of fitness. The principle of progression allows you to increase overload gradually without injury or discomfort.

The principle of specificity permits you to improve a specific component of physical fitness in specific body parts. To improve a specific component, you must select the appropriate physical activity. The overload for a given exercise will vary for each individual. Remember, injuries result when progression is not followed and overload is added too quickly.

Study Questions

True–false

Circle "T" for all correct statements and "F" for all incorrect ones.

T   F   1. When starting a physical fitness program, you do not need to consider your present fitness level.

T   F   2. To avoid injury, you should increase the intensity of your workout gradually.

T   F   3. If you increase the length of time of your exercise session, you will likely decrease the level of intensity.

T   F   4. Teenagers who are overweight may need to decrease the intensity of their workout as well as the length of time of their exercise session.

T   F   5. By applying the principle of specificity, you will increase leg strength by doing pull-ups.

Multiple choice

Place the letter of the best answer in the space provided.

_____ 6. Progression means
   A. slowly increasing the amount of exercise.
   B. changing from running to tennis.
   C. starting easy and going for a long period of time.
   D. starting fast to improve quickly.

_____ 7. The legendary Milo of Crotona became stronger due to applying the principle of
A. specificity.
B. all or none.
C. regression.
D. overload.

_____ 8. When you increase the workload of your training session, you are increasing
A. frequency.
B. intensity.
C. time.
D. specificity.

_____ 9. When you increase the length of your workout, you are increasing
A. frequency.
B. intensity.
C. time.
D. specificity.

_____ 10. Frequency basically means how
A. hard you exercise.
B. often you exercise.
C. long you exercise.
D. fast you exercise.

Discussion

11. Why must an overload be placed on the body to improve physical fitness?

12. Why will the amount of overload vary from individual to individual?

13. How did Milo of Crotona progressively increase his workload?

14. Why must you progressively increase the amount of work for improvement to occur?

15. Give an example of an exercise or activity you engage in and state how the principle of specificity is involved.

FLEXIBILITY 6

Chapter Objectives

As you read this chapter, look for answers to these key questions:

- Why is flexibility important?
- What is the difference between static stretching and dynamic stretching?
- How may the training principles be applied to improve flexibility?
- What safety precautions should be taken when you are engaging in flexibility exercises?
- How is flexibility evaluated?

When you have completed this chapter, you should understand the meaning of these vocabulary terms:

joint
ligament
muscle
tendon
static stretching
dynamic stretching
ballistic stretching
isostatic stretching

What Is Flexibility?

The rubber band theory applies to each of us; we will be no good until stretched.

What comes to your mind when the word flexibility is mentioned? Do you think of a circus acrobat tumbling about, a yoga instructor with legs behind his head, or someone doing splits? Everyone has flexibility to some degree, even the armchair athlete.

Flexibility is the ability to move body joints through a full range of motion. A **joint** is the point at which two bones come together. Examples of joints are the wrists, elbows, shoulders, hips, knees, and ankles. Notice that all joints do not move in the same way or degree. The amount of movement in a joint is limited by the way it is formed.

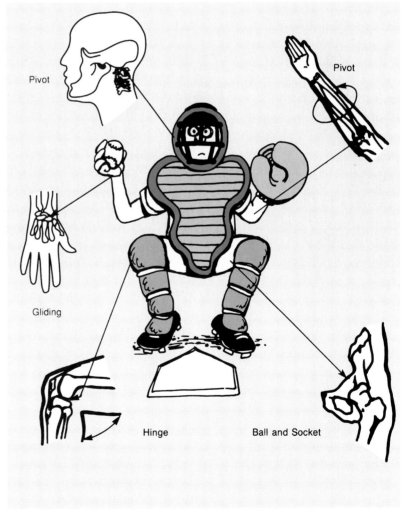

Joints of the human body

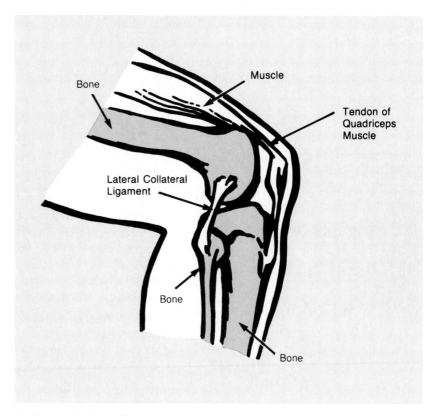

Soft tissue that limits flexibility

Pivot joints, such as the neck, permit a rotating motion. Hinge joints, such as the knee, permit a back and forth motion, while the hip and shoulders have a ball-and-socket formation, allowing for movement in many different directions. Your wrists and ankles have gliding joints which allow bones to slide over one another.

How is joint movement limited?

The direction in which a joint moves cannot be changed because of bone structure. For example, the bone structure of the elbow and knee joints set a very definite limit on how far the arm and leg can extend. These are mechanical factors that cannot be greatly modified. In other joints, such as the ankle and hip, the limitation on range of motion is imposed by *soft tissue* and is modifiable. This soft tissue is in the form of **ligaments, muscles,** and **tendons.** It is possible to improve the amount of motion in a joint by performing exercises that alter these soft tissues.

> Ligament: strong fibrous tissue which attaches one bone to another
> Muscle: meaty tissues surrounding bones
> Tendon: anchors the muscle to bone

To help you remember what makes up soft tissue, think of the terms in alphabetical order. First you have ligaments that attach bone to bone. Then muscles cover over or surround the bone. Finally, tendons anchor the muscle to the bone.

Why Is Flexibility Important?

A reasonable amount of flexibility (joint movement) is required to live a healthy and functional life both at work and play. Since the loss of flexibility occurs gradually, you probably will not realize you are experiencing a decrease in flexibility until a problem arises. Almost everyone has observed older adults and noticed that some are more flexible than others. This is due in part to the amount of activity in which they are presently engaged and past activity in which they were engaged.

Individuals of the same age may have different levels of flexibility due to past and present physical activity.

Reduces injuries

A lack of flexibility can result in joint or muscle injury during exercise or daily activities. While your strength and aerobic capacity will increase with exercise, your flexibility, in some cases, may decrease with weight training and aerobic conditioning. For this reason, every muscle strengthened must also be stretched to maintain and improve flexibility as much as possible. All athletes, including professional football players, now supplement their weight training conditioning programs with stretching exercises that improve flexibility and help reduce the number of injuries.

Prevents post-exercise pain

Post-exercise pain and stiffness caused by muscle spasms can be prevented or reduced by stretching exercises. Including warm-up and cool-down sessions in your workout will lengthen shortened muscles and, therefore, help prevent muscular soreness. The warm-up increases the blood supply to your muscles, raises their temperature, and makes them more flexible and resistant to injury. After exercising, a cool-down period of mild exercise can prevent muscle problems by gradually stretching the muscles that you have used and it can also prevent blood from pooling in the area exercised.

Reduces chance of low back pain

Low back pain is one of the most common ailments. It has been estimated that 80 percent of the population in the United States suffers from backaches. Adequate flexibility in the lower back and posterior thighs can do much to reduce these symptoms and prevent low back problems in adulthood.

Helps relieve emotional tension

Tight muscles arise from many causes—one is emotional tension. Stretching is one of the many exercises that can help relax tense muscles. Stretching the muscles in your neck, shoulders, and upper back is an especially useful way to relax because these muscles often become tense when you sit for long periods. Have you ever seen adults in an office stretch or bend their heads from side to side? Have you ever stretched your wrist and arm when taking a written exam? These movements are attempts to relieve tight muscles caused by tension.

Types of Stretching

Two types of stretching can safely be used to improve flexibility: static and dynamic. **Static stretching** is the more acceptable method of increasing flexibility. The process involves slowly moving the muscle to its stretching point and holding this position for 15 to 30 seconds. **Dynamic stretching** involves similar positions, but is done in a continuous, slow and controlled manner. This method of stretching should not be confused with ballistic or bouncing-type stretching in which the motion is done very rapidly. **Ballistic stretching** usually involves bobbing, bouncing, or jerky movements that use the body's momentum. This type of stretching is sometimes harmful because you may exceed the stretchable limits of the tissues involved.

One other type of stretching is called **isostatic stretching.** The initial phase of this type of stretching is static. You extend the stretch to the maximum limit and hold. After eight seconds, a partner pushes you beyond the initial limit as you relax. This form of stretching is not recommended because the helper does not know how much pain you are experiencing and may force a body part too far, causing injury.

Application of Training Principles

Stretching for relaxation can be performed anywhere at any time. However, to increase flexibility, you must engage in a more deliberate training program. This could be in the form of a separate flexibility program or combined with the warm-up and cool-down phase of your overall personal fitness program.

Remember, it is very important to raise the muscle temperature prior to stretching. This may be done by brisk walking, jogging, or other mild exercise. Increase muscle temperature before attempting any stretching exercises; otherwise, the flexibility exercises designed to prevent muscular problems may themselves cause problems.

Principle of overload

To improve flexibility, you must stretch the soft tissue (ligaments, muscles, and tendons) farther than you are accustomed. This additional overload can be placed on the body by an increase in frequency, intensity, or time of the exercise program.

FREQUENCY —Stretching exercises should be done a minimum of three times per week. Performing them daily is best.

INTENSITY —The muscle is stretched beyond its normal length to reach what is called the stretching point. To reach the stretching point, you slowly stretch until mild tension is felt.

TIME —The length of time a static stretching position is held may be increased gradually from fifteen to thirty seconds. Another way to increase time would be to increase the number of repetitions of an exercise, regardless of whether it is a static or dynamic stretch.

Hold stretch for a minimum of fifteen seconds.

Principle of progression

You may gradually increase the overload by increasing the (1) number of sessions per day or week (*frequency*), (2) distance the muscle is stretched (*intensity*), or (3) amount of time the position is held or the number of repetitions and sets (*time*). Regardless of how you progressively increase the overload, remember to do so in a slow, easy manner.

Principle of specificity

Stretching exercises will only improve flexibility in the joints you exercise. You may be flexible in one joint, but this does not mean you have the same degree of flexibility in all joints. Some of your joints may be unusually flexible, while others may be somewhat inflexible or of average flexibility. Flexibility is also specific to each individual. It has been found that females tend to be more flexible than males of the same age. Because flexibility differs with each person, you should not compete with how far others stretch. Some sports require flexibility in specific joints not required in other sports. Even within the same sport, flexibility requirements vary widely. For example, a quarterback needs shoulder-joint flexibility in order to throw a perfect pass, while a punter requires greater hip-joint flexibility.

Flexibility Safety Precautions

The following safety precautions should be considered when performing flexibility exercises:

1. All ballistic stretching exercises, which use the body's momentum to force a muscle beyond its stretching point, have the potential for causing injury and should be avoided.

2. Using partners to help you get extra stretch can cause injury because they do not know how much pain you are in and may force your body part too far.

Warning: Partner-assisted stretching can cause injury.

3. Start at a proper level and know when to increase the frequency, intensity, or amount of time of flexibility exercises.

4. There is danger of injury if you attempt to perform the same degree of stretching as someone else. Stretch according to what you feel, not according to what others do.

5. Include flexibility exercises with cardiovascular and muscular strength and endurance programs to prevent a muscle imbalance from occurring. For example, joggers frequently end up with tight hamstring muscles.

Flexibility Assessment

You should know your present level of flexibility before beginning an exercise program. Testing the flexibility of each joint would take too much time and require elaborate equipment. The flexibility tests described in the *Personal Fitness: Looking Good/Feeling Good Activities Handbook* will give you an indication of flexibility in joints most likely to need attention. A word of caution before you begin testing: (1) always warm up properly; (2) avoid ballistic (bouncing-type) movements when performing the tests; and (3) move into the testing position in a slow, controlled manner.

Flexibility Exercises

Upper body and torso stretch

Even if you score high on the flexibility tests, you should stretch your shoulders, lower back, hips, chest, backs of your thighs, and calves on a regular basis. You will need to select specific stretching exercises before engaging in an exercise session or sports activity. The following exercises stretch each of the different parts of the body and will serve as a starting point.

Upper body and torso stretch

- Bend the knees of both legs slightly
- Tuck the buttocks under to keep the spine in a straight line
- Slowly extend one arm overhead as high as possible while the other arm extends downward
- Keep the head straight; do not allow it to tilt back
- Hold for fifteen (15) seconds
- Repeat with other arm

Neck stretch

- Slowly bend your neck to the right and left
- Slowly turn your head to each side
- Lower your chin to your chest
- Rotate to the right and left
- *Never* bend your neck to the back (hyperextend)
- Hold each position for fifteen (15) seconds
- Emphasis should be on stretching in the various positions and not on rotation

Neck stretch

Triceps stretch

Triceps stretch

- Reach over your head toward your back with one hand
- Place the opposite hand on the elbow and apply steady pressure to the elbow
- Hold for fifteen (15) seconds
- Repeat with other arm

Chest and biceps stretch

- Grasp hands behind your back
- Slowly pull arms toward one another
- Hold for fifteen (15) seconds

Chest and biceps stretch

Shoulder stretch

Shoulder stretch

- Reach across your chest with one arm
- Slowly push this arm with your other hand
- Hold for fifteen (15) seconds
- Repeat with other arm

Three-prong support side stretch

- Kneel on one knee
- Bend to the same side as the bent knee and support part of your weight on one arm
- Extend the other leg out to the side
- Slowly extend the opposite arm over your head
- Stretch from the extended leg to the extended arm
- Hold for fifteen (15) seconds
- Repeat to the other side

Three-prong support side stretch

Lower back stretch

- Lie on your back
- Grasp legs underneath your knee caps
- Pull knees to your chest
- Hold for fifteen (15) seconds

Lower back stretch

Hamstring stretch

- Place one foot on a low step or bench
- Keep the knee bent, and bend from the hips
- Hold for fifteen (15) seconds
- Repeat with other leg

Hamstring stretch

Groin stretch

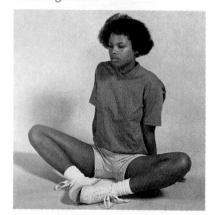

- Sit on floor and place the soles of your feet together
- Pull your feet a comfortable distance into your groin
- Place hands on the floor to your side to support the back
- Slowly press the knees down
- When you feel tension, hold for fifteen (15) seconds

Groin stretch

Quadriceps stretch

Quadriceps stretch

- Place left hand on partner's shoulder or other object for balance
- Flex right leg backwards
- Grasp right ankle with your right hand
- Press the foot into your hand
- Do not pull on the foot or touch the heel to buttocks as this will cause strain on the knee ligament
- When you feel the stretch in the front of the leg, hold for fifteen (15) seconds
- Repeat for left leg

Calf stretch

Calf stretch

- Stand slightly more than arms' length from a wall
- Place feet shoulder width apart and flat
- Hands should be flat, with knees and body straight
- Lean forward by bending the elbows
- When you feel tension in the lower calves, hold for fifteen (15) seconds

Achilles' tendon stretch

Achilles' tendon stretch

- Stand 2 to 3 feet from a support
- Place one foot behind the other
- Lean forward keeping the heels flat
- Slowly bend the knee of the rear leg until the Achilles' tendon is stretched
- Hold for fifteen (15) seconds
- Repeat with other foot

Shin stretch

Shin stretch

- Stand 2 feet from a support
- Place one foot behind the other
- Bend the knee of the rear leg with toes to the ground
- Slowly bend until you feel a stretch in the front of the lower leg
- Hold for fifteen (15) seconds
- Repeat with other leg

Harmful Stretching Positions

The following stretching positions can be harmful. Many of them put stress on your joints, ligaments, tendons, and muscles and may lead to injury. If you choose to perform any of the exercises listed, remember to stretch in a safe and controlled manner. Always avoid rapid, jerky, bouncy, ballistic movements since they may cause injury.

Head circles

Never hyperextend your neck or do full head circles.

Head Circles

Arm circles

Arm circles are actually ballistic stretches of the shoulder joint.

Plow

The plow position compresses the cervical vertebrae of the back and puts a large amount of stress on the lower back.

Arm circles

Plow

Sitting quadriceps stretch

Sitting on your heels to stretch the quadriceps overbends the knee joint.

Sitting quadriceps stretch

Four-count toe touch

The four-count toe touch is a traditional exercise that has been done for years, so it may be difficult to remove from your workout. Just remember that many safe alternatives do not place undue pressure on the disks of the lower spine. Also, some people tend to lock their knees as they reach downward. This can hyperextend the knee joint and cause an injury.

Four-count toe touch

Hurdle stretch

The hurdle stretch forces sideway movement of a hinge joint (bent knee joint) that is only meant for flexion and extension.

Deep knee bends

Bending at the knees is essential for safe lifting techniques. However, while keeping the heels flat on the ground, your knees should not bend beyond the point at which your thighs are parallel to the floor (more than 90 degrees). Going beyond this limit may cause injury to any of the structures around the knee, including cartilage.

Hurdle stretch

Deep knee bends

Summary

Flexibility is the ability to move body joints through a full range of motion. The direction of joint movement is limited by the way it is structured. Some joints have a very limited range of motion, while others allow for movement in all directions. The four types of joints are the pivot, hinge, ball-and-socket, and gliding joint. Flexibility improvement can be made by performing static stretching, if the limitation on range of motion is imposed by soft tissues (ligaments, muscles, and tendons).

Everyone needs flexibility to some degree both at work and play. An adequate degree of flexibility can reduce injuries, prevent post-exercise pain, reduce chance of low back pain, and help in relieving emotional tension.

Static and dynamic stretching can be used to improve flexibility. These stretches can be done as part of the warm-up and cool-down phases of your overall personal fitness program or as a separate flexibility program.

All principles of training are important in the development of flexibility. You should assess your present level of flexibility before beginning the flexibility phase of your personal fitness program.

Ballistic stretching and exercises that hyperextend the neck should not be performed. In addition, activities that compress the vertebrae, overbend a joint, or force sideward movements should be avoided.

Study Questions

True–false

Circle "T" for all correct statements and "F" for all incorrect ones.

T   F   1. Individuals with good flexibility are less likely to be injured.

T   F   2. You should bounce as hard as you can when doing flexibility exercises.

T   F   3. Ligaments help hold joints together.

T   F   4. Tendons attach muscles to bones.

T   F   5. Poor muscle development, poor flexibility, or poor posture are factors contributing to the fact that 80 percent of people in the USA suffer from "low back pain".

Multiple choice

Place the letter of the correct answer in the space provided.

_____ 6. Stretching exercises will help
A. avoid injuries.
B. build strength.
C. develop cardiovascular endurance.
D. none of the above.

_____ 7. Joints can be prepared for vigorous physical activity by doing
A. push-ups.
B. sit-ups.
C. stretching.
D. weight training.

_____ 8. Muscles and other connective tissues should be stretched
   A. three times per week.
   B. only before jogging.
   C. once a week.
   D. when it is cold.

_____ 9. To increase flexibility, you must overload the muscle by
   A. increasing your running distance.
   B. lifting heavy weights.
   C. performing isometric exercises.
   D. stretching farther than normal.

_____ 10. Which exercise below is a safe exercise for developing flexibility?
   A. Achilles' tendon stretch
   B. deep knee bends
   C. four-count toe touch
   D. hurdle stretch

Discussion

11. Why does a person lose flexibility?

12. What is the major difference between static and dynamic stretching?

13. How can the overload principle be used to improve flexibility?

14. Why should you not use partners when performing stretching exercises?

15. Name a sport or recreational activity in which you participate. List three stretching exercises you could perform to warm up for this activity.

CARDIOVASCULAR FITNESS 7

Chapter Objectives

As you read this chapter, look for answers to these key questions:

- How can you measure your pulse rate?

- What benefits are gained from participation in activities promoting cardiovascular fitness?

- How does aerobic exercise help prevent cardiovascular disease?

- How can the training principles be applied to improve cardiovascular fitness?

- How do you determine the rate at which your heart should be exercised?

- How do you know when it is safe to progress with your cardiovascular training?

When you have completed this chapter, you should understand the meaning of these vocabulary terms:

pulse	maximum heart rate
resting heart rate	target heart rate
recovery heart rate	aerobic
blood pressure	anaerobic
atherosclerosis	

Why Is Cardiovascular Fitness Important?

The race is not always to the swift but to those who keep on trying.

Cardiovascular fitness is said to be the most important of all physical fitness components. No matter how strong you might look, if your circulatory and respiratory systems cannot meet your muscles' demand for oxygen, you cannot continue activity for a long period of time.

Developing cardiovascular fitness will help you enjoy life to its fullest.

Exercising to improve cardiovascular fitness will increase your energy level, making it possible for you to exercise longer without tiring, and making you feel good. Additionally, exercising for cardiovascular fitness will help you look good, since the exercises will help you control your weight, improve your appearance, and improve your ability to meet the problems you face daily. You may be one of many people who have a low level of cardiovascular fitness if you find you are short of breath, tire easily, are unable to swim, run, bike or perform physical activities as others do.

If you are short of breath and left behind, you need to improve your cardiovascular fitness.

Cardiovascular fitness is the body's ability to provide oxygen continuously to muscles as work is performed over an extended period of time. This component of fitness includes the circulatory system (heart, blood, and blood vessels) and the respiratory system (lungs and air passages).

Research has shown that body functions improve with use and decline with disuse. In other words, the heart, lungs, and muscles become stronger and more efficient in their utilization of oxygen as they are used more. To understand how to improve your cardiovascular fitness, you must first understand how the circulatory and respiratory systems function and what diseases may result if these areas are neglected.

Circulatory and Respiratory System

People often take oxygen for granted and never think of it as fuel for the body. The fact is, the more oxygen muscles receive, the more energy they can produce and the better you feel. The circulatory and respiratory systems work together in providing muscles with necessary oxygen. As air is breathed in, the blood picks up oxygen from the lungs and carries it to the heart.

The heart is a remarkable muscle that actually serves as two pumps. The ventricle on the left side of the heart force blood containing oxygen throughout the body through elastic blood vessels called arteries. Arteries always carry blood away from the heart.

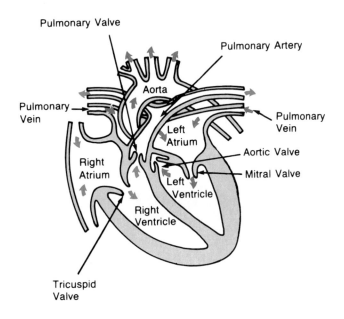

Pulmonary Valve

Pulmonary Artery

Aorta

Pulmonary Vein

Pulmonary Vein

Left Atrium

Aortic Valve

Mitral Valve

Right Atrium

Left Ventricle

Right Ventricle

Tricuspid Valve

Cross section of the heart. Note the left ventricle muscle walls are thicker than the right ventricle walls, since this chamber pumps blood throughout the body compared to the right ventricle, which only has to pump it to the nearby lungs.

As arteries branch out in the body, they gradually decrease in size until they form tiny capillaries. This is where food and oxygen are delivered from the blood to cells throughout the body. Notice how the capillaries serve as bridges between arteries and veins. Veins always carry blood toward the heart.

Just as ashes are left after a fire, some waste materials remain when cells use up oxygen. These wastes are picked up by the blood in the capillaries and are transported back to the heart by veins. Blood is forced through the veins by contracting muscles. The blood in veins can only move toward the heart, because one-way valves keep the blood from flowing backward when the muscle relaxes. The right ventricle of the heart pump the returning blood to the lungs, where wastes are exchanged for more oxygen and the process repeats itself.

Your body holds only about 12 pints of blood. Therefore, the blood must circulate throughout the body to supply all the body cells continuously with oxygen and nutrients and to remove wastes. That is why the heart, blood vessels and blood are called the circulatory system.

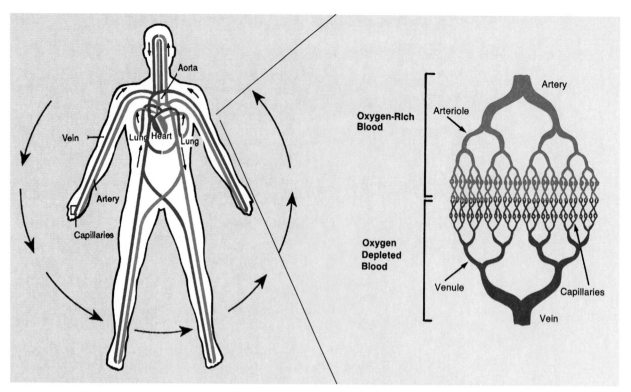

Simplified map of circulatory system. Arrows indicate blood flow out of the heart through arteries and back by way of veins.

Capillaries. Blood travels from arteries and arterioles into capillaries and then into venules and veins.

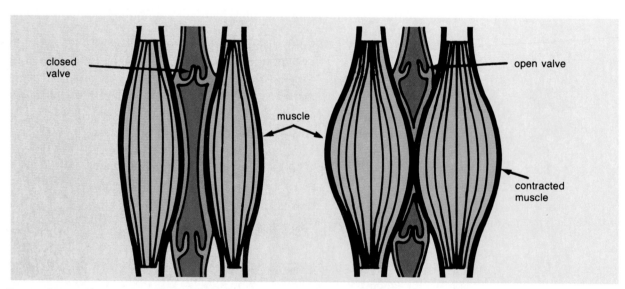

Contracting muscles squeeze the blood through one-way valves toward the heart.

Monitoring the Heart

How fast does the heart beat to pump blood? Your heart rate varies with the changing needs of your body. When you are lying down, your heart rate will be less than when you are standing. Running will produce a higher heart rate than when you are doing a less vigorous activity, such as walking. Your size also has an effect upon your heart rate. The average heart rate for adults is 70 beats per minute. In children, the heart beats about 100 times per minute. It is important for you to know how hard your heart muscle is working. One method is to measure your pulse rate.

Pulse

Your **pulse** is caused by pressure of the blood on the artery wall, and it corresponds to your heart beat. The best locations for measuring your pulse rate are at the *wrist* and *neck*, where arteries lie just below the skin. To take your pulse at the wrist, place your index and middle finger against the skin at the base of your thumb on the soft area of the wrist.

Pulse may be taken at the wrist or carotid artery. Take the pulse for ten seconds and multiply by six for a one-minute heart rate count.

To measure your pulse rate at the carotid artery of the neck, move your index and middle fingers from the ear lobe midway toward your Adam's apple. Once you have located the pulse, count it for six (6) seconds and place a zero at the end of that number, or take it for ten (10) seconds and multiply by six (6) to obtain a one-minute pulse rate.

Several factors may cause the pulse rate to vary. For example, exercise increases the pulse. The higher the intensity of exercise, the higher the pulse rate. Other factors that may affect the pulse rate include excitement, position of the body, and illness. Since your pulse rate varies throughout the day, it is recommended that you take your pulse at rest if you wish to compare pulse rate readings.

Resting heart rate

Since the heart is a muscle, it becomes stronger when exercised. By keeping a record of your resting heart rate, you can measure the progress gained in your cardiovascular fitness program. An active person has a lower resting heart rate than someone who is inactive. The heart of an active person pumps more blood with each beat, thus working more efficiently. After a few months of cardiovascular training, a sedentary person will note a decrease in the resting heart rate of ten to twenty-five beats per minute. This illustrates that your heart is becoming stronger and more efficient.

To measure the **resting heart rate,** take your pulse just after waking in the morning and before getting out of bed. Your pulse should be taken while you are in a sitting or lying position. A range of 50–100 beats per minute for resting heart rate has been established as normal by the American Heart Association. However, research shows that adults with resting heart rates over 70 have a greater risk of heart attack than those with resting heart rates below 70.

Resting heart rate should be taken first thing in the morning and in the same position.

Recovery heart rate

To determine when it is safe to progress in your training program, you should check your pulse after the exercise session to determine your **recovery heart rate.** The guiding principle is that your heart rate should drop to about 120 beats per minute (BPM) within 5 minutes after the workout and be less than 100 beats per minute after 10 minutes.

5 minutes after exercise = 120 BPM
10 minutes after exercise = 100 BPM

If after five minutes your pulse does not drop to 120 beats per minute, or after ten minutes to 100 beats per minute, you need to reduce the intensity of your workout. On the other hand, you may elect to increase the intensity of your workout if your recovery heart rate is below 120 beats per minute five minutes after exercising and below 100 beats per minute after ten minutes.

Monitor recovery heart rate to determine when to progress in your training program.

Blood pressure

Blood pressure is the measure of blood force against the walls of the arteries. Blood pressure is recorded with two numbers. The higher number recorded is the *systolic pressure* and is your blood pressure at the moment blood is pumped from the heart by the ventricles. The lower number is the *diastolic pressure* and represents the blood pressure when the heart is relaxed and filling with blood. The normal range for blood pressure is stated as:

systolic pressure   120 + or −
diastolic pressure   80 + or −

Blood pressure is one external method of monitoring your circulatory system. A high reading indicates an inefficient system.

Aerobic exercises contribute to blood pressure control. Both systolic and diastolic pressures can be reduced as a result of aerobic training. Long-term research studies have shown that the lower the blood pressure, within normal limits (100/70), the lower the risk of having a heart attack.

Cardiovascular Disease

When people are young, they have a tendency to feel indestructable. Many teenagers believe they will live forever and give little thought to illnesses, much less death. What is needed is a mature evaluation of your lifestyle and how it will affect your health in twenty or thirty years. Scientists have found that many illnesses affecting older people start very early in life.

One illness that starts at an early age is cardiovascular disease, which is the major cause of death (43 percent) in the United States. To put it another way, for every American who dies of cancer, the second ranking cause of death, two die of a heart-related illness.

Causes of cardiovascular disease

The primary cause of cardiovascular disease is a buildup of fatty deposits on the inner walls of the arteries. These deposits cause an arterial passageway to become smaller, leading to a condition called **atherosclerosis.** This restricts the blood flow, much like placing your thumb over a garden hose restricts the flow of water. Just as your

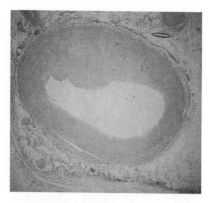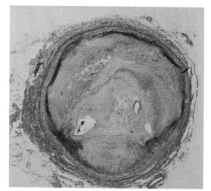

Developing stages of atherosclerosis

thumb causes a higher water pressure in the hose, the fatty deposits on the inner walls of the arteries cause a higher blood pressure, which makes the heart work harder.

These fatty deposits can become so great that blood will not flow through the artery. In addition, blood vessels can also be blocked by a blood clot (thrombosis) lodging in a narrowed passageway. When this happens to an artery that feeds the heart (coronary artery), a heart attack occurs. When it happens to an artery that supplies blood to the brain, a stroke occurs. While a heart attack or stroke happens suddenly, the factors causing the blocked arteries can be traced back to many years earlier.

Risk factors

A study of medical records indicates that ailments of the heart and blood vessels have decreased in recent years. However, cardiovascular disease continues to hold the deadly distinction of being the number one killer in the United States. In fact, heart and blood vessel diseases cause almost as many deaths as cancer, accidents, pneumonia, influenza, and all other causes of death. As you will recall from Chapter 1, the risk factors associated with heart attacks are:

1. Inactivity
2. Obesity
3. High Blood Pressure
4. High Levels of Cholesterol
5. Stress and Tension
6. Smoking
7. Sex of Individual
8. Heredity
9. Age

As you review the nine risk factors, notice that the first six are controllable. The choices you make today in your lifestyle will have an effect on how well and how long you live when you are older. In fact, many people your parents' age and older wish they had learned the values of exercise and other good health habits when they were much younger.

Cardiovascular Benefits of Exercise

Participating in activities that promote cardiovascular fitness strengthens the heart and reduces atherosclerosis. Active people are better able to clear fats from their blood stream as a result of exercise. Therefore, fatty substances are less likely to form on the walls of the arteries. Research has shown that active people have less heart disease and are less likely to die from a heart attack than inactive people.

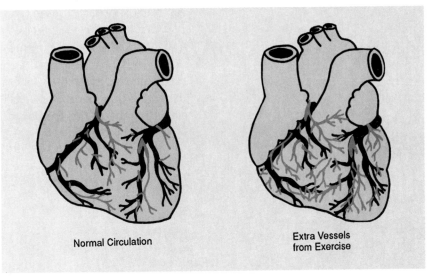

Normal Circulation

Extra Vessels
from Exercise

Research has shown that people who engage in regular exercise develop extra arteries in the heart muscle.

Everyone would like to have enough energy to take part in a favorite sport or activity without feeling tired. One way to obtain additional energy is to increase the oxygen supply to muscles by exercising the heart. Your heart muscle gets stronger as you engage in cardiovascular activities. Thus, it works more efficiently because it is able to pump out more blood with each beat. In addition, the trained heart beats fewer times per minute when compared to the heart of someone who is not physically fit. The result is that the muscles receive more oxygen and do not tire as easily.

Not only do you lessen your chances of developing heart disease and make your cardiovascular system more efficient through training, you can also obtain mental benefits. Concentration, ability to cope with stress, and positive self-concept are also improved.

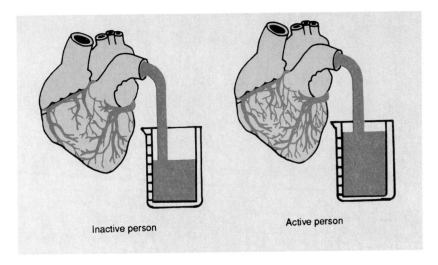

Inactive person

Active person

The active person's heart is able to pump out more blood with each beat.

Application of Training Principles

The main purpose of any cardiovascular fitness program is to increase the body's ability to utilize oxygen. To increase cardiovascular fitness you must engage in exercises that involve movements of the large muscles of the body. You must be able to maintain these exercises continuously for at least fifteen to thirty minutes. Such exercises are called aerobic, since the working muscles continue to receive as much oxygen as they need. Brisk walking or jogging are activities that would meet the above requirements.

Considerable research has led to the development of the principles of training. By following these principles, you will be able to train efficiently and avoid possible strain and injury.

Principle of overload

One way to increase the oxygen supply to the muscles is to develop the muscle that serves as the pump. Since the heart is a muscle, it responds to training, as do all other muscles.

To develop the heart muscle, you must push it beyond its normal range and make it pump more blood with each beat. This additional overload can be placed on the heart by an increase in the frequency, intensity, or time of the exercise program.

Bicycling is an aerobic activity and will develop cardiovascular fitness.

FREQUENCY —The exercise selected must be performed regularly to reach an adequate level of cardiovascular fitness. Ideally, your training program will become a daily habit; however, benefits can be achieved with fewer workouts.

Since the heart is a muscle, it can be made stronger just as any other muscle.

Aerobic activities must be performed at least three times per week to reach an adequate level of cardiovascular fitness.

As a beginner you may elect to walk, swim, or bike three days per week, then increase the overload by doing your selected activity four days, then five days, and finally on a daily basis. Participating in such activities two days per week will not significantly increase cardiovascular fitness. However, such a schedule may maintain the level you have acquired.

INTENSITY —In cardiovascular training you are trying to strengthen the heart and improve the body's ability to utilize oxygen. Even though the heart is a muscle, you cannot observe it getting stronger, as you can the biceps. Therefore, you must rely upon the pulse rate, which is an external sign of the heart's condition, since it corresponds exactly to the beat of the heart.

The intensity of a cardiovascular activity may be determined by the response of the pulse rate. How much you increase the heart rate is the critical question. If you do not increase it enough, little or no improvement in cardiovascular fitness will occur. On the other hand, exercising too hard too soon may cause extreme discomfort.

Each person has a **maximum heart rate** which should not be exceeded. To determine your maximum heart rate, subtract your age from 220. To obtain the greatest cardiovascular benefits, the American College of Sports Medicine recommends that the intensity of your training be sufficient to increase your heart rate to 60–90% of maximum heart rate or at 50–85% of heart rate reserve. They also recommend that aerobic activities be performed three times per week for 20–60 minutes to reach an adequate level of cardiovascular fitness.

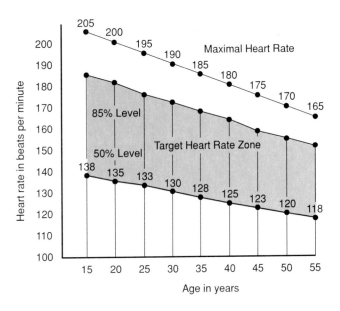

As age increases, maximum attainable heart rate decreases, thus affecting the upper and lower levels of the target heart-rate zone.

The 50 to 85 percent range of your heart rate reserve is termed the **target heart-rate zone** and is the desired level of intensity for most people. However, you should start at a lower percentage if you have not been active for some time or are overweight. While you will not obtain all of the benefits of aerobic training, some improvement will occur. For example, start at a 40 percent target heart rate and gradually progress to the 50 to 85 percent range. The chart also illustrates the target heart-rate zone for various ages using 70 beats per minute as the resting heart rate.

To compute your target heart-rate zone, you must first determine your own maximum heart rate. Remember, to obtain this figure subtract your age from 220. Your resting heart rate is then subtracted from your maximum heart rate. This value is multiplied by the lower percent at which you wish to train and is added to the resting heart rate.

$$[(220 - \text{age}) - \text{resting heart rate}] \times 50 \text{ percent} + \text{resting heart rate} = \text{lower level of target heart rate zone}$$

The above formula should be used again to obtain the upper limit of your target heart-rate zone. Eighty five percent would be substituted in the formula in place of the 50 percent lower limit.

Below is an example of how Chris figured the lower and upper limits of his target heart-rate zone. Chris is 14 years old and his resting heart rate is 70.

	Lower Limit	Upper Limit
1. He subtracted 14 (age) from 220 to obtain his maximum heart rate of 206. 220 − age = maximum heart rate.	220 − 14 206 MHR	220 − 14 206 MHR
2. Using the method described in this chapter, he determined his resting heart rate to be 70, which was subtracted from 206.	− 70 RHR 136	− 70 RHR 136
3. Chris decided that 50% should be the lower limit of his target heart rate zone and that 85% would be a safe upper limit for training effect.	× 50%	× 85%
4. He multiplied Step 3 times the value of Step 2.	68	122.4
5. Chris then added his resting heart rate.	+ 70 RHR	+ 70 RHR
6. It was determined that 138 was the lower limit of his target heart-rate zone and 186 was the safe upper limit.	**138**	**185.6**

Once the target heart-rate zone is known, you will be able to check the intensity of your exercise by stopping briefly from time to time to count your pulse rate. Many people find it difficult to utilize this information, since they have to count their pulse for ten seconds and then multiply by six for a one-minute count (60 seconds). This may be hard to do if you are swimming in a pool or jogging two miles from home. A helpful hint is to use a pencil and paper to divide the lower and upper limits of your target heart rate zone by six. This will give you a ten-second count that can be easily remembered. For example, if your target heart rate lower limit is 151 and your upper limit is 192, divide both by six. The ten-second count would be 25 for the lower limit, and 32 for the upper limit.

While exercising, if your pulse falls below the lower limit of your target heart-rate zone, you should increase your intensity (*speed up your pace*). If your pulse goes above the upper limit of your target heart-rate zone, decrease your intensity (*slow down your pace*).

TIME —To achieve all the values of cardiovascular training, you must maintain the target heart rate (50 to 85 percent of your maximum heart rate reserve) for a minimum of 20 minutes. A beginner may find it necessary to start a program involving less time and progressively increase the length of time of the exercise session.

To increase the overload, you may choose to increase the pace (intensity) or the distance (time) jogged. For example, after weeks of 20-minute exercise sessions, in which you were steadily increasing your pace (intensity) to keep your pulse in the target heart-rate zone, you might choose to increase your distance (time) and decrease your pace (intensity). Remember, as time is increased, intensity will decrease.

The chart below summarizes a typical aerobic exercise session. As you will note, this individual has a normal heart rate of 70 beats per minute. After a five- to ten-minute warm-up, the individual gradually increases

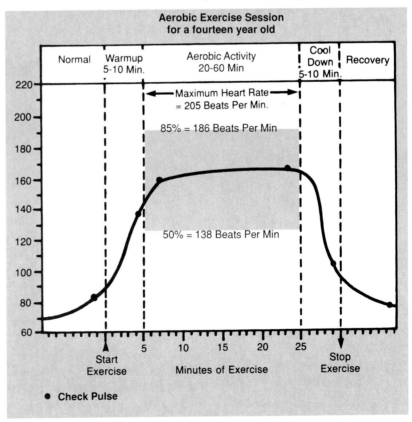

Heart rate during a typical aerobic exercise session

Progressively add overload.

her heart rate to 140 beats per minute, which is at the lower level of the target heart-rate zone. She slightly increases the heart rate and maintains it within the target heart-rate zone of 138 to 186 beats per minute. This level of activity is maintained for 20 to 60 minutes. At the conclusion of the training period, she begins her cool-down session to gradually reduce the heart rate. After the cool-down, she begins the recovery stage, with the heart returning to its pre-activity level.

Principle of progression

Since the heart adjusts to the workload you place on it, the overload must be periodically increased in order for improvement to occur. For example, if you begin a regular exercise program that involves jogging one mile in nine minutes, you might find the workout stressful. Your cardiovascular fitness would gradually improve if you continued the nine-minute rate. But after several weeks of jogging the same distance in the same time, cardiovascular improvement would stop and adaptation would occur. To continue improving your cardiovascular fitness, you would have to increase the stress by jogging a mile in a shorter period of time. This progressive increase in the overload would place additional stress on your cardiovascular system and produce additional improvement.

Remember to observe your target heart rate and recovery heart rate. If while training, your heart rate goes above or below your target heart rate zone, adjustments need to be made. Also, you need to reduce the intensity or duration of your training program if your recovery heart rate is not less than 120 beats per minute five minutes after exercising or less than 100 beats per minute ten minutes after exercising.

Principle of specificity

Aerobic exercise promotes cardiovascular fitness better than any other type of activity. **Aerobic** means *with oxygen* and involves activities that can be performed for at least fifteen minutes without gasping to catch your breath. Examples of aerobic activities include jogging, dancing, swimming, bicycling, racquetball, and soccer.

Anaerobic (*without oxygen*) activity is performing at a pace which uses oxygen faster than the body can replenish it. Since this is true, anaerobic exercise can be done only for a short period of time. Examples would be the 220-yard dash or the 50-yard freestyle swimming events. What other events would be considered anaerobic? Aerobic?

Summary

Cardiovascular fitness includes the efficient operation of the circulatory and respiratory systems. These systems improve with use and decline with disuse. Thus, the more active you are, the more energy you will have, and the more your chances of developing cardiovascular disease will decrease.

One important element of cardiovascular fitness is the efficiency of the heart, since it pumps oxygen-rich blood to the muscles. Because your heart is a muscle, it becomes stronger when exercised. Aerobic activities, such as swimming and jogging, will provide a training effect when maintained for a minimum of fifteen minutes and performed at least three days per week.

You must rely on your pulse rate to determine the effect of training. By calculating your *resting heart rate, target heart rate zone, and recovery heart rate,* you will know where to begin, and with careful monitoring during your training session, you will know when to progress.

Having a high level of energy is one of the most important benefits of exercise. Without energy, it is very hard to feel good about yourself. While following a sound cardiovascular fitness program may not always be easy, the payoff can be most rewarding. **Here's to healthy hearts.**

Study Questions

Multiple choice

Place the letter of the best answer in the space provided.

_____ 1. When you increase the pace of your run, you are increasing
   A. frequency.
   B. intensity.
   C. time.
   D. none of the above.

_____ 2. In order for jogging to contribute toward the development of cardiovascular fitness, your target heart rate must be maintained for at least:
   A. three minutes.
   B. five minutes.
   C. ten minutes.
   D. twenty minutes.

_____ 3. What is *not* a primary benefit of regular cardiovascular exercise?
   A. increased ability to take in oxygen
   B. improved balance
   C. lower blood pressure
   D. lower pulse rate

_____ 4. Which of the blood vessels have one-way valves?
   A. arteries
   B. capillaries
   C. veins
   D. both A and C

_____ 5. Blood flow in the body follows the pattern of
    A. heart to arteries to capillaries to veins.
    B. heart to arteries to veins to capillaries.
    C. heart to veins to arteries to capillaries.
    D. veins to capillaries to heart to arteries.

_____ 6. Your friend, who is age 15 and has a resting heart rate of 70, wishes to start a jogging program. What would you suggest as a proper starting target heart rate?
    A. 115
    B. 138
    C. 155
    D. 178

_____ 7. What should your training heart rate be in order to safely develop cardiovascular fitness?
    A. 140 bpm
    B. 50 percent
    C. 95 percent
    D. 190 bpm

_____ 8. Which of the following is an appropriate cardiovascular fitness training activity?
    A. football
    B. 100 yd dash
    C. swimming
    D. weight lifting

_____ 9. The intensity of your workout is too difficult if your heart rate has not returned to 120 bpm within how many minutes?
    A. 2 minutes
    B. 5 minutes
    C. 10 minutes
    D. 15 minutes

_____ 10. What is the minimum number of days per week a person should exercise to improve cardiovascular fitness?
    A. one
    B. three
    C. five
    D. seven

Discussion

11. How does cardiovascular fitness allow you to exercise longer?

12. What type of activities are best for developing cardiovascular fitness? Why?

13. You currently can jog one mile in twelve minutes, but you have a personal goal of jogging two miles in twenty minutes. How would you train to reach your goal?

14. Why should your pulse rate be taken after an exercise session?

15. Review the personal goals you developed in Chapter 3. Did any of your goals focus upon improvement of cardiovascular fitness? If not, develop a goal for cardiovascular fitness improvement.

MUSCULAR FITNESS 8

Chapter Objectives

As you read this chapter, look for answers to these key questions:

- What is the difference between muscular strength and muscular endurance?

- How will a weight-training program affect males and females differently?

- What two types of fibers are found in skeletal muscles?

- How can the training principles be applied to improve muscular strength and muscular endurance?

- What are the primary differences between muscular strength and muscular endurance training?

- What safety practices should you follow when lifting weights?

When you have completed this chapter, you should understand the meaning of these vocabulary terms:

atrophy
slow-twitch fibers
fast-twitch fibers
isometric exercises
isotonic exercises

isokinetic exercises
repetition
resistance
set

Muscular Strength and Endurance

Muscular fitness includes two health-related components of physical fitness: muscular strength and muscular endurance. Muscular strength is the ability of a muscle group to apply a maximal force against a resistance one time. Also, the term resistance in weight training simply refers to the weight lifted. Muscular endurance is the ability to repeat muscle movement over a period of time.

To look good and feel good, you must have adequate muscular fitness. Why do two people with the same weight and height but with different amounts of muscle and body fat look different? The person with more muscle looks trimmer because muscle is more dense than fat. One pound of muscle takes up less space than one pound of fat. Another reason is that toned muscles do not allow protruding in areas such as the abdomen.

Another factor influencing your appearance is good posture. Developing your body's muscles will help you have the strength and endurance to carry your body in an upright position. Good posture makes anyone look better. Do you know someone who does not stand up straight? Compare that person with someone who does.

Strong muscles not only improve your appearance, but also help you perform physical activity better. Additionally, strong muscles help to reduce fatigue, avoid back pain, and prevent muscle injuries and muscle soreness.

Myths About Weight Training

Some people may tell you that weight training makes a person muscle-bound or inflexible. Others say muscular fitness is good for men, but unfeminine for women. Still others tell you that muscles will turn into fat if you stop training. Of course, none of these myths is correct.

Muscle-bound physique

Years ago body builders encouraged men to do exercises that often made them muscle-bound. Such individuals did not do flexibility exercises or perform their strength training exercises properly. As a result, they lost some of the range of motion in certain joints. Becoming muscle-bound is not a problem when weight-training exercises are performed properly.

Females will gain many benefits from a muscular fitness program.

Is weight training good for females?

Those who believe strength training is good for males, but not for females are incorrect. Females have *estrogen,* rather than *testosterone,* as their primary sex hormone. This one factor eliminates the chance of a female developing bulging muscles while training with weights. Females also should not be concerned about dramatic changes in muscle definition, since they have an average of eight percent more body fat than males, which masks muscle definition. A female can realize all the benefits of weight training without worrying about muscle bulk and definition. Good muscular fitness is just as important for women as it is for men, since both will appear more attractive and physically fit.

Can muscle turn into fat?

A major misconception about weight training is that muscle will turn into fat when you stop lifting weights. Muscle does not turn into fat, nor does fat turn into muscle. Muscle is muscle and fat is fat. What really happens is that muscles **atrophy,** or become smaller, when they are not used. Muscle atrophy can easily be seen when an arm becomes thinner after being placed in a cast for several weeks. An increase of fat will occur only if you continue to take in more calories than you burn.

There is about as much truth to fat turning into muscle as muscle turning into fat.

Muscle Fiber Composition

While muscular strength and endurance are closely related, they are separate components of health-related fitness. To understand how to apply the three principles of training to strength and endurance, you must first understand that different muscle fibers are involved in these two health-related components.

Skeletal muscles are attached to bones by tendons. When they contract or shorten, they produce movement. There are two types of skeletal muscle fibers, fast-twitch and slow-twitch. Both types of fibers are found in all skeletal muscles. Heredity determines the number of fast-twitch and slow-twitch fibers you possess. However, you can improve both the fitness and performance level of each kind of fiber with appropriate exercises.

Slow-twitch fibers

Slow-twitch fibers are also called *red* fibers because of the large amount of blood supply directed to them. Such fibers are slow to contract but have the ability to continue contracting for long periods of time. These fibers are best suited for aerobic or muscular endurance activities, since they do not tire easily. Slow-twitch fibers enable individuals to run long distances or repeat muscular tasks many times. It is because slow-twitch fibers contract slowly and do not tire easily that thousands of runners complete the Boston Marathon.

Fast-twitch fibers

Another name for **fast-twitch fibers** is *white* fibers. These fibers contract quickly, allowing explosive muscular contractions and, therefore, lend themselves more readily to anaerobic, or strength related, activities. An example of a person who needs a large number of fast-twitch fibers is a sprinter. This athlete must react quickly at the sound of the starting pistol. Fast-twitch fibers fatigue easily.

Methods of Developing Muscular Fitness

As in strengthening the heart, a skeletal muscle becomes stronger when it works harder than it has been accustomed to working. Three types of exercises provide resistance to make the muscle work harder for the purpose of developing muscular fitness: **isometric, isotonic,** and **isokinetic.**

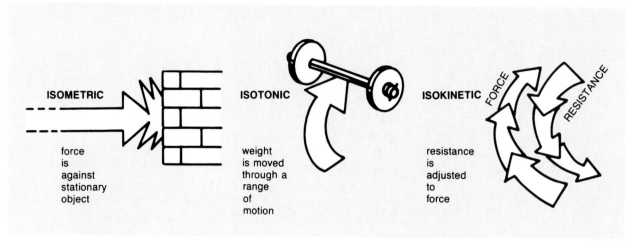

Types of resistance exercises

Isometrics

In **isometric exercises,** you contract, or tighten, your muscles but do not change their length. Therefore, there is no movement of the body part or object against which the force is exerted. To perform an isometric exercise you would push against a stationary object or against another part of your body that prevents movement. For instance, place a tennis ball in your hand and squeeze it as hard as possible for a period of 6 to 8 seconds. This is one example of an isometric exercise.

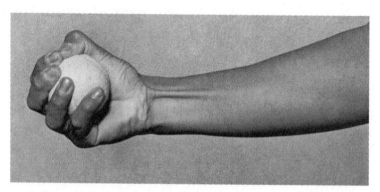

Grip strength can be improved through isometric exercises.

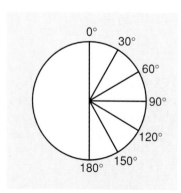

During isometric contractions, strength is developed only at one fixed position within a muscle's full range of movement.

Strength improvement will result from isometric contraction. However, strength is developed only at the position the exercise is performed. Strength is not developed throughout the entire range of movement, which includes many possible positions. For example, if you are performing an isometric arm exercise, you will only develop strength at that specific angle. Your arm goes through many different angles when fully extending and flexing. It would be impossible to exercise all positions effectively utilizing isometric principles. Therefore, these exercises are the least effective in developing strength and endurance.

Isometric exercises can be hazardous for older persons, or for those with high blood pressure and other circulatory ailments. Such exercises temporarily impair circulation of the blood and cause the blood pressure to rise. Also since isometrics provide no movement, muscular endurance and flexibility are not improved.

There are a few advantages of isometric exercises. They require no special equipment and are useful for people with certain physical disabilities and people confined to a small space. For example, isometrics can be done while sitting at a desk or while riding in a car.

Isometric exercises may be used to develop strength when temporarily or permanently disabled.

Isotonic exercises

Isotonic exercises are those in which the muscle lengthens and shortens through its full range of movement while lowering and raising a resistance. The resistance may be in the form of a barbell (weight training) or your own body weight (calisthenics). An isotonic contraction can be observed when you lift a glass of water to drink. The biceps muscle on the front of the arm contracts and shortens, causing the elbow to bend. To lower the glass, the bicep muscle relaxes and lengthens. Another example is when a barbell is raised and lowered through a muscle's full range of movement.

Increase resistance by adding weights.

Strength varies according to the
angle of the joint.

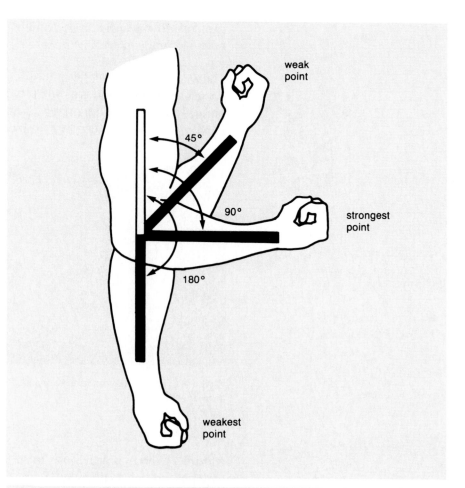

Weight machines with cams
provide variable resistance
through the full range of motion.

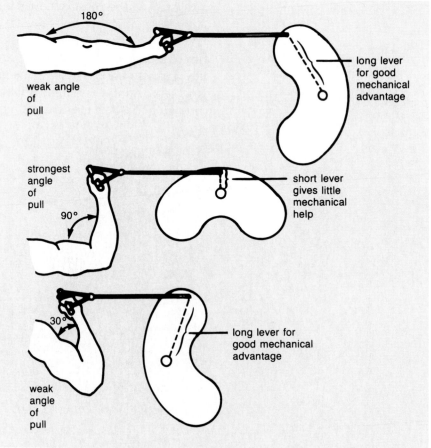

With isotonic exercise, the actual amount of weight the muscle will be able to lift varies throughout the range of motion. Therefore, the heaviest amount of weight you will be able to lift will be equal to the capacity of your limb at the weakest joint position throughout the total range of movement. For example, at a 90-degree joint angle you may be able to lift 80 pounds, while at a 160-degree angle you may be able to lift only 40 pounds. The 160-degree joint angle limitation means you will only be able to lift 40 pounds throughout the full range of motion. This amount of weight might not be sufficient to overload the strongest joint position. Despite this drawback, isotonic exercises are excellent muscular fitness developers.

Isokinetic exercises

As just mentioned, a muscle has different levels of strength while moving through a complete range of motion. In other words, the angle at which the muscle is pulling on the bone determines the amount of weight you can lift.

Isokinetic exercises, with the use of specially designed machines, overcome the disadvantages of isometric and isotonic exercises. The isokinetic machine mechanically allows you to overload a muscle with maximum resistance throughout the muscle's entire range of movement at a constant speed. The obvious advantage of this method is that maximum resistance is provided at the stronger angles, while less resistance is provided at the weaker angles.

Currently, there are no "true" isokinetic weight training machines in fitness centers that provide both constant speed and constant resistance. Many fitness centers do, however, have variable resistance weight machines which provide varying resistance throughout a complete range of motion. As the cable moves over the irregularly shaped cam, the resistance is adjusted in accordance with the lever characteristics of a specific joint movement.

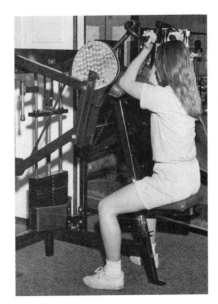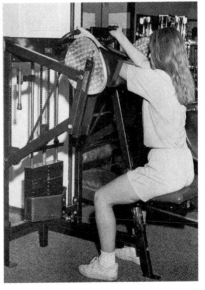

Variable weight machines provide maximum resistance throughout the entire range of motion.

Application of Training Principles

The type of exercises and equipment used influence the method in which you apply training principles to muscular strength and endurance development. Since isometric exercises have many disadvantages and isokinetic exercises require expensive equipment not readily available in the home, the application of training principles in this chapter is limited to the use of isotonic exercises.

Remember, fast-twitch fibers allow you to perform strength-related tasks, and slow-twitch fibers allow you to do muscular endurance activities. To develop these different types of muscle fibers, you can perform many of the same exercises. The primary difference in muscular strength and muscular endurance training is in the amount of weight and the number of times it is lifted.

Principle of overload

To improve muscular fitness, you must deal with three factors. First you must *stimulate* the muscle. This is accomplished by placing an overload on the muscle, making it work harder than normal. The second factor is *nutrition.* In order for a muscle to grow, it must receive adequate nutrients, which will be discussed in the following chapter. After the muscle has been overloaded and given the necessary nutrients, the muscle must be given time to *rest,* which is the third factor necessary for muscle development.

As in the case with the other health-related components, overload can be placed on the body to increase muscular strength and endurance through the application of frequency, intensity, or time (FIT).

FREQUENCY —Remember, once your muscles have been stimulated by some form of resistance, such as lifting weights, they must be given time to grow. You must spend sufficient time resting between training sessions to allow this growth to occur. Most authorities agree that 48 hours are required. Therefore, muscles should be exercised every other day, not daily.

Some weight lifters prefer to work out every day. They accomplish this by working different muscle groups on alternating days. For example, one day they may work the upper body and the next day work the muscles in the lower body.

INTENSITY —Intensity of a weight training program is called the resistance and is determined by the amount of weight you lift. While you must increase resistance to improve muscular strength and endurance, it is important to remember that the increase must be gradual.

The intensity or amount of weight you would lift to improve muscular strength should be 60 to 90 percent of what you could lift one time. On the other hand, the amount of weight lifted to improve muscular endurance would be 30 to 50 percent of what you could lift one time. For example, if you can lift 100 pounds one time, and wish to improve muscular strength you would train with a barbell weighing 60 to 90 pounds. If your intent was to improve muscular endurance, you would use a 30- to 50-pound barbell. It is generally accepted that exercising against a resistance more than 60 percent of your maximum is a form of strength training, and anything less is a form of endurance training.

Sample Workout
Muscular Strength Development

Exercise	Goal	S E T	Date				
			9-1	9-3	9-5	9-8*	9-10**
Front Curl	40 lbs.	1	40 / 4	40 / 6	40 / 8	40 / 8	50 / 6
		2	40 / 4	40 / 6	40 / 6	40 / 8	50 / 4
	8 reps.	3	40 / 4	40 / 6	40 / 6	40 / 8	50 / 4

Muscular Endurance Development

Exercise	Goal	S E T	Date				
			9-1	9-3	9-5	9-8*	9-10**
Front Curl	15 lbs.	1	15 / 12	15 / 16	15 / 20	15 / 20	20 / 18
		2	15 / 12	15 / 14	15 / 18	15 / 20	20 / 12
	20 reps.	3	15 / 12	15 / 14	15 / 18	15 / 20	20 / 12

*goal achieved for all three sets
**weight increased, repetitions lowered

TIME—This refers primarily to the number of times the exercise is performed. A **repetition** is the completion of a single, full-range movement of the body part being exercised. In other words, each time you lift a barbell or do a calisthenic exercise, you are performing one repetition. A group of repetitions performed one after the other is called a **set.** Usually, a person who is beginning a weight-training program will perform three sets of repetitions with at least two minutes of rest between each set.

A. *Muscular endurance*—To develop muscular endurance the resistance (intensity) should be low and the number of repetitions (time) high. Three sets of 12 to 20 repetitions would need to be performed for a pure muscular endurance program.

B. *Muscular strength*—Whereas muscular endurance is developed with the use of light weights and many repetitions, muscular strength is developed with the use of heavy weights and few repetitions. Three sets of 4 to 8 repetitions would need to be performed for maximum strength gain.

Principle of progression

You now know you must overload muscles to improve muscular strength and endurance. Since your body adapts to lifting the same amount of weight, you must gradually lift more. If you try lifting too much too soon, you run the risk of muscle or joint injury.

Remember, you should perform three sets of 4 to 8 repetitions to improve muscular strength. You start with the maximum amount of weight you can lift four times for all three sets. If you cannot lift this amount four times during the third set, you need to decrease the amount of weight. As you make progress and are able to lift the amount of weight eight times for all three sets, you should add additional weight and drop your number of repetitions back to four per set. To improve muscular endurance, you use the same approach only with less weight and more repetitions (12 to 20 per set).

Principle of specificity

You must overload the specific muscle you want to improve. If you want to increase leg strength, you must do leg exercises. You will not improve your leg strength by doing arm exercises. The more you can target or isolate the muscle you want to improve, the better the results.

To achieve best results, select the appropriate exercise and place your body and/or body parts in a certain position to isolate the muscle. This will force the targeted muscle to do the intended work rather than having the work spread over a number of secondary muscle movers. The standing biceps curl is a good example of how to isolate

Performing curl against wall to target biceps

a muscle group. By standing next to a wall, you can greatly reduce the influence of the legs and hips, forcing the biceps to do the work. This technique results in more strength being gained in the targeted area.

Remember, any weight training program must be designed to meet your specific needs and goals. You will have to design a specific program to achieve specific results regardless of whether you are trying to improve strength, add bulk, improve muscle tone, or lose weight.

The American College of Sports Medicine recommends resistance training that is of moderate intensity, sufficient to develop and maintain fat-free weight. They also recommend at least one set of 8-12 repetitions of eight to ten exercises that work the major muscle groups at least two days per week.

Weight Training Considerations

Regardless of the type of training program, safety should always be a major consideration. When engaging in weight training programs, you should always take the necessary steps to reduce the risk of injury. One of the most important precautions is to train with a partner, who could serve as a spotter and keep you from being pinned under a weight. You should also:

1. Warm up properly before you begin any physical conditioning program.

2. Concentrate on endurance when beginning a weight training program. The lighter weights will give you an opportunity to learn how to perform the exercises correctly. In addition, the endurance training will prepare your body for higher intensity strength training.

3. Check barbell plates before you lift to make sure they are properly secured and will not slip off.

Tighten barbell collars before lifting.

4. Keep hands dry for a good grip.

5. Hold the bar or machine hand grips comfortably, since a tight grasp may cause your blood pressure to increase.

6. Exhale when pushing against the resistance (blow the weight up) and inhale when lowering the weight. Holding your breath will cause a dramatic increase in your blood pressure and may damage some blood vessels. Although people argue about the correct way to breathe, the most important consideration is not to hold your breath.

7. Use correct form at all times to prevent injury and to achieve greatest gains from the exercise. Reduce the weight if you cannot maintain control during the exercise.

8. Keep the weight close to the body when lifting it from the floor to your chest.

9. Space your feet shoulder-width apart to provide balance and to help spread the load of the weight.

10. Keep the back straight, with hips below the shoulders. This will help prevent straining the back muscles.

11. Go through the complete range of motion to increase flexibility.

12. Exercise large muscle groups first, then the smaller groups.

13. Exercise muscles on both sides of the joint to ensure muscle balance.

14. Lift the weight on a count of two. Lower it more slowly, to a count of four.

15. Always do lifts or exercises in the same sequence from workout to workout. In this way, fatigue is relatively the same at various points throughout the workout because activities are done in the same order.

16. Do not perform the bench press or other lifts unless spotters are present. If you lose control without a spotter present, you could be pinned under the weight.

17. Avoid a deep-knee bend or full squat position when performing exercises. You will lessen the chance of knee injury and achieve good results by doing the exercise with one-half knee bends.

Muscular Fitness Exercises

Shoulders

The following exercises primarily develop the muscles of the shoulder region.

standing lateral raise

Stand erect with feet spread shoulder width apart. Grasp a 5- to 10-pound dumbbell in each hand with palms inward. Raise the dumbbells sideways to a position directly overhead. Keep the arms straight throughout. Return to starting position and repeat.

Standing lateral raise

shoulder shrug

Stand straight holding the barbell in front of the upper thighs, arms straight, using an overhand grip with hands close together. Shrug shoulders as if trying to touch your ears. Return to starting position and repeat.

Shoulder shrug   Upright rowing

upright rowing

Stand erect, holding the barbell in front of the thighs with overhand grip and hands close together. Pull the bar to chin level while bending the elbows completely, keeping elbows higher than hands. Lower to starting position and repeat.

Arms

The following exercises develop the muscles of the arms and hands.

front curl

Hold bar with palms facing out. Lift weight forward and upward, bending arms completely. Lower to starting position with arms fully extended before repeating. No other motion should be allowed with elbows or back.

Front curl

reverse curl

Execute in the same manner as front curls except use a reverse grip (palms facing the body).

Reverse curl

two-arm press

Stand erect holding the barbell in front of the chest with palms facing forward while pressing the weight above the head until the arms are straight. Lower the weight and repeat.

Two-arm press

triceps extension

Using one arm, lift a weight above your head. Keeping elbow close to your head, bend the elbow and lower weight behind the head. Straighten the arm and return to starting position.

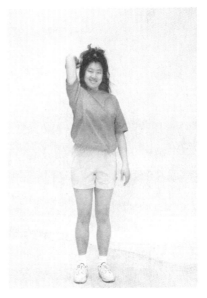

Triceps extension

triceps press (french curl)

Same as triceps extension except you use a barbell to exercise both arms. The back should be straight with barbell held overhead and palms facing forward, 8 to 12 inches apart. Lower the weight to the neck and repeat.

Triceps press (French curl)

wrist curls

Grasp the barbell with your hands shoulder width apart using an underhand grip. Sit and support your forearms on your thighs. Raise and lower the weight by curling hands and wrists.

Wrist curls

reverse wrist curl

This movement is performed the same as a wrist curl, except an overhand grip is used.

Reverse wrist curl

Chest

The following exercises primarily develop the muscles of the chest region.

bench press

Lie face up on the bench. With the arms in the extended position lower the bar to the chest and return to the extended position. **CAUTION**: Spotters should always be used for this exercise. Without a spotter, you could be pinned under the weight.

Bench press

flies

Lie face up on the bench with knees bent and feet flat on the floor. Hold a weight in each hand (palms inward). Slowly lower the weights until arms are parallel to the floor. Keeping the arms straight, raise the weights until they touch above you.

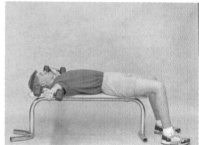

Flies

one-arm raising

Stand with your right foot ahead of your left, with weight in right hand. Bend forward so that upper body is approximately parallel to floor. Grasp something with free hand for balance. Lift the weight upward to side of the chest, pause, then lower to starting position. Repeat with left arm.

One-arm raising

Lower Back

The following exercise primarily develops the muscles of the lower back region.

side leg lifts

Lie on your left side and raise your right foot upward. Lie on right side and repeat with left leg. A freezer bag filled with beans or leg weights may be used to provide added resistance.

Side leg lifts

Abdominals

The following exercise primarily develops the muscles of the abdominal region.

bent-knee sit-ups

Lie flat on your back with arms folded across your chest and hands touching opposite shoulders. Bend your knees at a 90-degree angle. Your heels should be 12 to 18 inches from the buttocks. Curl up to a sitting position, first with the head, then the shoulders, and finally the back. Uncurl and return to starting position. You may progressively increase the number of repetitions (time) and/or the resistance (intensity) by holding a weight on the chest or by lying head downward on an incline board.

Bent-knee sit-up

Sit-up using incline board

Sit-up using incline board holding weight on chest

Thighs

The following exercise primarily develops the muscles of the thigh region.

half-knee bends

Beware of doing full squats, since knee injury can result. To begin the lift, stand straight, feet parallel and shoulder-width apart, with barbell resting across the shoulders. You may wish to wrap a towel around the bar if it is too uncomfortable on the shoulders. Keeping the back straight, squat to one-half knee bend and return to the starting position. Heels should maintain contact with the floor at all times.

Half-knee bends

Summary

There are many benefits to be derived from muscular fitness. You not only become stronger and reduce fatigue, but you also avoid muscular soreness and injuries.

Both males and females can benefit from muscular strength and endurance exercises. Females need not be concerned about developing bulky muscles, as they have different hormones and a larger percent of body fat than males. Remember, fat is fat and muscle is muscle. Muscle can never turn into fat.

There are two types of skeletal muscle fibers. Slow-twitch or red fibers provide the body with the ability to do muscular endurance or aerobic activities. Fast-twitch or white fibers enable the body to do muscular strength or anaerobic activities.

While muscular strength and muscular endurance are closely related, they are separate components of fitness. The primary difference in training for the two components is in the amount of weight and number of times a resistance is lifted.

Study Questions

True–false

Circle "T" for all correct statements and "F" for all incorrect ones.

T   F   1. Muscle turns into fat when you stop a weight training program.

T   F   2. The number of times you exercise per week determines the number of fast-twitch and slow-twitch fibers you have.

T   F   3. Isometric exercises are recommended for an older person or those with high blood pressure, since they involve no heavy lifting.

T   F   4. Isokinetic exercises require the use of expensive machines.

T   F   5. You should lift heavy weights a few repetitions during each training session to develop muscular strength.

T   F   6. You should perform your lifts in the same sequence from workout to workout.

T   F   7. You should hold your breath when lifting the weight and breathe in when lowering it.

T   F   8. The person with more muscle looks trimmer because muscle is more dense than fat, thus taking up less space than fat.

T   F   9. Females will not develop bulging muscles or experience muscle definition as males do, since testosterone is females' primary sex hormone.

T   F   10. The difference in muscular strength and muscular endurance training is in the amount and number of times a weight is lifted.

Discussion

11. Why do females not need to be concerned about developing bulging muscles?

12. Briefly discuss the differences between isometric, isotonic, and isokinetic exercises. Which ones are you most likely to perform?

13. Explain how the training techniques to develop muscular strength and muscular endurance differ.

14. List five steps that will reduce the injury risk of weight training.

15. Review the personal goals you developed in Chapter 3. Did any of your goals focus upon improvement of muscular fitness? If not, develop a goal for improvement of muscular fitness.

NUTRITION 9

Chapter Objectives

As you read this chapter, look for answers to these key questions:

- How did you develop your current nutritional habits?

- What is food's relationship to health?

- What are the essential nutrients, and why does the body need them?

- What are the health problems that might occur from bad diet decisions about essential nutrients?

- Why is water such an important element of our diet?

- What is the new food label, and how is it supposed to help you plan a nutritionally balanced diet?

- What is the food guide pyramid?

- How should the food guide pyramid be used to plan a balanced diet?

- How should you determine your daily calorie requirements?

When you have completed this chapter, you should understand the meaning of these vocabulary terms:

fad diets	**LDL**
proteins	**minerals**
carbohydrates	**fat-soluble vitamins**
saturated fat	**water-soluble vitamins**
unsaturated fats	**food guide pyramid**
HDL	**basal metabolism**

You are what you eat.

Both males and females want to have a better physique, clear complexion, and glossy hair. Teenagers are especially interested in physical fitness and the greater ability to compete in athletic contests. None of these goals can be achieved without good health, and good health cannot be separated from good nutrition. To be in good health means that you feel like doing the things you want to do, such as racing a friend across the pool, skiing on the slopes, or merely getting through a hectic day. When one has plenty of vigor and vitality, second thoughts are not given to the energy required to complete a desired task. Keeping yourself in a condition which enables you to meet these situations each day cheerfully and eagerly is what nutrition is all about.

Sound nutrition is important if you want to lead an active, enjoyable lifestyle.

Historical Use of Food

The original concern for food was to survive. In ancient times, nearly all of man's day was spent searching for food by hunting, fishing, or scavenging. Later, when man learned to raise and store food supplies, food was used as the centerpiece of social and religious ceremonies. Today, we use food in a variety of ways in addition to supplying our bodies with the essential nutrients. For example, food is used during social occasions, fellowship with friends, or as an escape when we are disappointed, sad, or depressed. Many of the ways we now utilize food does not contribute to a balanced and nutritional diet and may lead to dietary problems.

Acquired Experiences with Food

Why do you choose the foods that you eat? Why do you like one food, and your best friend likes another? Have you ever stopped to think why you and your family do not eat the type of food that other people eat, such as food that is popular in another country? Most people select the type of food they eat with little thought. Sure, you may say you want a pizza or a cheeseburger, but why do you like and choose them rather than some other foods? We eat and like the foods included in our diet for many reasons. The strongest factor is probably our family. We normally eat and like what our family eats and likes. We have been eating what our families prepared since we were born and have been conditioned to like it without ever having the opportunity to make decisions about those foods.

In addition to family influences, friends and our ethnic background are also strong factors that determine the food content of our diets. When you grow older and change your family situation, you will begin having the opportunity to make your own decisions about what and how you eat. You will make new friends when you go to college, who like foods that you have never eaten before. Your friends will try to get you to taste some foods they like. Perhaps some of your new friends will be from different ethnic backgrounds and will help you develop a broader selection of foods that you enjoy.

Your ethnic background has a strong influence on your nutritional decisions.

Lifestyle also determines what we eat. Are you rushed to get from school to soccer practice, or to a music lesson, or to a game? Stop and think about how a busy lifestyle affects what you eat. Fast foods were developed for people who did not have a lot of time to make their own meals. The microwave is another invention that affects what we eat, since we may be too busy to take time to cook.

Other factors such as the cost of food, advertisements, the region of the country you live in, or your religious preference will all have some influence on the type of foods you eat. You need to be sure that these factors are not influencing you to eat just one type of food. You can hold on to your ethnic traditions or your religious traditions and still maintain a balanced diet.

Food and Its Relation to Health

"You are what you eat" is an old saying that may not be too far from the truth. Food and how you relate to it will have a great impact on your lifestyle. What do you think of when you hear the word "food"? Perhaps you think of your favorite meal or your favorite snack. Perhaps you think of social events and having fun. Do you think of food as fuel? Food is the fuel that keeps your body going. Food is the energy source for an active, vigorous, and fun lifestyle. If we do not eat enough of this energy source in the right proportions, we may not have the energy needed to enable us to be active. However, too much of a good thing is not that good either.

Too much food leads to health problems associated with being too heavy. Also, if we eat too much food that is high in cholesterol or other fats, these foods may also cause health problems. Health problems may also occur if your diet lacks one or more of the essential nutrients described later in this chapter. Having clear skin is a common goal for most teenagers. Many complexion problems are caused by an imbalance of chemicals in the body, and a balanced diet may be able to help.

Nutrition effects the way your hair, teeth, and skin look.

Diets that promote weight loss without practicing sound nutritional practices may be considered fad diets. Health problems occur with many of the fad diets that you see on television or read about in the newspapers. Individuals have become seriously ill by depriving their body of essential nutrients over a long period of time because of a "special diet." No diet can cause a person to lose weight unless there is a lower calorie intake than caloric expenditure for the body to draw on energy stores for metabolism. This negative caloric balance must not put one's health in jeopardy by eliminating any of the essential nutrients. Fad diets, which restrict one's intake to only one food, such as eggs or rice, are harmful. No one food contains all the nutrients necessary for a healthy lifestyle. Even milk, the one nearly perfect food, is low in iron and other nutrients. Good nutritional status requires that the proper balance and quantities of essential nutrients be obtained from a mixed diet of many possible food combinations.

Essential Nutrients

Your body needs certain essential nutrients to function properly. These nutrients are *carbohydrates, fats, protein, minerals, vitamins, and water.* An adequate amount of each of these nutrients in your diet is essential for good health and your ability to maintain a balanced exercise program. The food you eat will be the primary source for your essential nutrients. Many people take vitamins and other dietary supplements, but most of us could save that money if we eat a balanced diet.

If you do not have a sufficient amount of carbohydrates in your diet, your body will use proteins for energy rather than for muscle building.

148

Proteins

Proteins are the building blocks of the body and are extremely important when you are considering exercise to build muscle. Protein is present in every cell of the body. The most important function of protein is its role in the growth and repair of your body's tissues. Protein can also supply energy when there are not enough carbohydrates or fat in the diet. Foods in the meat group are the main dietary source of protein.

proteins are made of amino acids

Protein is made up of chemical substances known as **amino acids.** Amino acids are essential in the digestive process. Twenty-one different amino acids have been identified. The body is able to make some amino acids from other food sources, but there are at least nine amino acids that cannot be manufactured in the body. These are referred to as **essential amino acids.** *Essential amino acids* must be included in your diet, with meats and animal products being the primary source. Soybeans are also an excellent source of amino acids. If you decide not to eat red meat or animal products, your diet can still be balanced to contain all of the essential amino acids by including a mixture of the right beans, peas, nuts, seeds, etc. However, the balance is much harder to achieve, and a few vegetarians experience health problems because they are not careful enough.

animal proteins

Complete proteins include such animal products as meat, milk, and eggs. These animal products contain an excellent balance of amino acids required for a healthy diet. In the United States and Canada, animal products are a staple food source, and there are few examples of individuals suffering from a lack of protein in their diet.

non-meat protein

In many parts of the world, protein is not obtained from animal products, but are provided by such sources as dried beans or rice. Since these are not good sources of the essential amino acids, it is not uncommon in such places to see many cases of stunted growth, seriously low body weight, slow recovery from illness, lack of vitality, and lack of muscle tone.

Carbohydrates

Carbohydrates serve as the "fuel" for our active, vigorous lifestyle and are obtained from breads, cereals, fruits, and concentrated sweets. They are the best source of energy. Carbohydrates can be used by the body easily and quickly, and are used first, before fats or proteins. Many teenagers, and especially athletes, give up carbohydrates in an attempt to lose weight. When teenagers eliminate carbohydrates, they usually have problems developing strength or muscle bulk, even though they are eating a large quantity of protein. In other words, when a person eliminates carbohydrates from his diet, the body will then use protein for fuel, instead of using the protein for body building.

starches and sugars

There are two types of carbohydrates, **starches and sugar.** Glucose is "blood sugar" and is the primary source of energy for the cells of the body. Have you ever become light headed when you have not eaten for a while? That is because you experienced low blood sugar, and the brain tissues were hungry, or were being deprived of their fuel supply.

Starchy carbohydrates such as bread, potatoes, and cereals provide a good source of energy and contain a variety of nutrients. Sugary carbohydrates, like those found in soft drinks and candies, have few, if any, nutrients and are called "empty calorie" food. Fruits and fruit juices are the best way of getting additional sugar in your diet, since they contain other essential nutrients that our body needs.

Carbohydrates are the most efficient fuel for your body.

fiber

The undigestible material that makes up the walls of plant cells is known as **fiber.** Fiber is another kind of carbohydrate. Fiber is useful in helping move waste through the body system and is helpful in lowering the risk of several diseases, including colon cancer. There are several different types of fiber; therefore, you should eat a variety of foods that contain fiber. Common sources of fiber include whole grain breads, cereals, fruits, and vegetables. As the fiber content of your diet is increased, you should also increase your fluid intake. However, fiber should not be viewed as the "cure all" of nutrition. Adding fiber to a nutritionally poor diet will not enhance the diet and may have an adverse effect.

Fats

Fat yields twice as much energy as protein or carbohydrates but is not as easy to use as carbohydrates. Foods containing fat are divided into two major groups: *animal fats and vegetable fats.* Animal fats have a high **saturated fat** content and are found in meat, poultry, milk, cheese, ice cream, and egg yolks. Vegetable fats are **unsaturated fats** and are found in margarine, salad dressing, mayonnaise, cooking oils, avocadoes, olives, and nuts. Saturated and unsaturated fats are important because of their effects on the cholesterol level in the blood.

cholesterol

Cholesterol is a wax-like fatty substance that is produced by the body in the liver and is used for building cells. In healthy people, the body will produce all the cholesterol that is needed. However, when you eat animal products high in saturated fats such as meat, cheese, and eggs, you consume additional cholesterol. Cholesterol is transported throughout the body in the blood stream, with excess amounts stored on the walls of the blood vessels. Excessive amounts of cholesterol in the circulatory system, which requires storage, results in blocked arteries that limit blood flow to the brain and heart.

HDL and LDL

There are both "good" cholesterol and "bad" cholesterol. The good type is called **HDL** (high density lipoprotein), while the bad type is **LDL** (low density lipoprotein). It is believed that the good HDL helps remove the extra cholesterol, while the bad LDL leads to the buildup of cholesterol on the artery walls. It is believed cholesterol levels of greater than 180–200 places a person in danger of developing blocked blood vessels. Although the total amount of cholesterol in the blood is related to health dangers, the real concern is the ratio of HDL to LDL. Our goal should be to have no more than three times the amount of bad cholesterol (LDL) than we have good cholesterol (HDL).

There are both good and bad cholesterol. The "good" HDLs are the body's police that help remove the "bad" LDLs from the blood stream.

The amount of total cholesterol in the body is closely related to diet, heredity, and the amount of regular vigorous exercise. It is believed that regular vigorous exercise and heredity are the major factors in determining the amount of HDL that you have in your blood. Remember, HDL helps remove cholesterol from the blood, so we want to do everything possible to develop HDL. There are no foods that contain HDL. Therefore, you can only increase the ratio of HDL to LDL by exercising and decreasing your intake of saturated fats.

Minerals

When someone says your body needs **minerals,** you probably think of minerals found in the ground. In truth, the minerals needed by the body are taken from the ground. This is accomplished by eating plants or animals that have eaten plants.

There are twenty minerals that are necessary to perform body functions. Each of these are needed in very small amounts or serious deficiencies and diseases may occur. None of the minerals are destroyed by cooking, but some will be dissolved into the liquid. If the liquid is thrown away, those minerals may be lost. The more important ones are discussed below.

Calcium and phosphorus are used for the development of bones and teeth as well as for muscular development. They are also used in the work of the muscles and the nervous system. Milk is a food rich in calcium.

Iron is combined with protein to form hemoglobin, an essential element of the blood. Good sources of iron are meats, green leafy vegetables, apricots, prunes, whole-grain, and enriched cereals.

Iodine is essential for proper functioning of the thyroid. This mineral is available in iodized salt, sea food, and fruits and vegetables grown in soil along sea coasts.

Potassium helps to maintain your heartbeat, water balance, nerve transmission, and the breakdown of carbohydrates and proteins.

Sodium is a mineral that helps the body maintain a proper balance of body fluid and plays a major role in nervous transmission, cardiac function, and normal metabolism. However, excessive amounts of sodium may lead to abnormal fluid retention, which is related to hypertension. A balanced diet will normally provide all of the sodium that you need.

Vitamins

Vitamins are organic, chemical substances found in very small amounts in food. You only need small amounts for normal growth and maintenance of the body. They do not supply energy but aid in utilization and absorption of nutrients. For example, vitamins are required so that the body can use carbohydrates, fats, and proteins for energy and all other normal functioning of the body organs. Sometimes several vi-

Many people waste money on vitamin supplements. A balanced diet will provide the required vitamins for most people.

tamins must work in combination with one another for a specific body function. The absence of one of these needed vitamins will prohibit the reaction from occurring. One vitamin cannot be substituted for another. All vitamins can be dissolved. Some are soluble in fat and some in water.

fat-soluble vitamins

Some vitamins can be stored in fat deposits of the body and are called **fat-soluble vitamins.** It is critical that you do not take large supplemental doses of these vitamins, since an over supply of these vitamins stored in the body could cause toxicity. The most important fat-soluble vitamins include vitamin A, vitamin D, vitamin E, and vitamin K.

water-soluble vitamins

Many vitamins that our bodies require for proper functioning will dissolve in water and, therefore, cannot be stored in the body tissue. When the body takes in more of these vitamins than it can use immediately, the extra vitamins are excreted in the urine and lost. These vitamins must be contained in our daily diet. You should also be careful in food preparation, since **water-soluble vitamins** will dissolve into the liquid used for food preparation. If this liquid is thrown away, the vitamins will be lost. You should limit the amount of water used in cooking and then try to incorporate that liquid into the meal. Overcooking also destroys the vitamin content in foods.

Water-soluable vitamins are lost when foods are cooked and the liquid is poured down the drain.

consumer concerns regarding vitamins

Advertisements on radio and television, or in newspapers and magazines promote the idea that multi-vitamin pills and mineral concentrates are necessary as part of our diet. The advertisers promote this view by stating that we need to make up for the lack of nutrients in modern processed foods or the lack of time to have three balanced meals a day. The truth is that many vitamins cannot be stored by the body, and any taken in excess will simply be excreted in the urine. If the ones that can be stored are taken in large doses, toxicity may result. The good life cannot be gained from a bottle of vitamins. The result usually is just the opposite: money spent and possible harm to one's health.

balanced approach to vitamins

The best approach to providing the body with the proper amount of vitamins is eating a balanced diet. If a person is deficient in a particular vitamin, a balanced diet will not correct the situation, and supplements may have to be taken. In such cases, however, a physician should be consulted.

Water: An Essential Substance

Water is essential for your body and makes up about 65 percent of your weight. Although you may not think of water as a nutrient, it is essential for normal functioning of the body. You can live longer without food than water, since water is the primary component of blood and tissue fluids.

Water carries dissolved waste products from the body, helps digest food, and carries nutrients throughout the body. It also is critical to temperature control. You lose some of your body's mineral and water content when you perspire heavily. Heat illnesses can result if you fail to drink enough water before, during, and after strenuous activities. Remember, you need to drink one cup of water every 20 minutes when you are exercising to avoid heat related problems. Everyone should drink at least two quarts of water a day.

The New Food Label

Many people have had difficulty determining the nutritional value of certain foods and were unable to compare the contents of two food products. The old labels were difficult to understand and were not consistent from one product to another. In an attempt to correct this problem and aid consumers in making the best nutritional decisions, the federal government is requiring producers to carry a standardized food label on all food products.

The new food label will make it easier for consumers to make comparisons and quickly determine the specific nutritional value of each product. The label will look the same on all food products, contain the same information, and provide that information in a standardized form. The new food label includes a number of new requirements that were not always included on previous food labels. The illustration, Nutrition Facts, identifies features of the new food label.

HOW TO READ A FOOD LABEL

1. Serving Size
Serving size and number of servings in the container is given in easily understood measures. This makes it easier to compare similar products and know the serving sizes are basically identical.

2. Calories and Fat
The total number of calories per serving and the amount of fat per serving is provided.

3. Percent Daily Values
The percent Daily Values for key ingredients is based on a standardized daily diet of 2000 calories. This section of the label helps the consumer determine the foods that are high or low in the required daily nutrients.

4. Vitamins and Minerals
Provides information about four important vitamins and minerals: Vitamin A, Vitamin C, Calcium, and Iron.

5. Suggested Daily Value
The bottom portion of the panel presents the Daily Value that should be consumed. Figures for a 2000 and 2500 diet are provided for comparison.

6. Health Benefits
The number of calories contained in a single gram of fat, carbohydrate, and protein are provided. This helps the consumer determine if food has potential for lowering cancer risk.

Bran Cereal

Nutrition Facts

Serving Size ½ cup (58g)
Servings Per Container about 8

Amount Per Serving

Calories 200

Calories from Fat 10

	% Daily Value*
Total Fat 1g	2%
Saturated Fat 0g	0%
Cholesterol 0mg	0%
Sodium 350mg	15%
Potassium 160mg	5%
Total Carbohydrate 47g	16%
Dietary Fiber 5g	21%
Sugars 7g	
Other Carbohydrate 35g	
Protein 6g	

Vitamin A 25%	●	Vitamin C 0%
Calcium 2%	●	Iron 45%
Vitamin D 10%	●	Thiamin 25%
Riboflavin		25%
Niacin 25%	●	Vitamin B6 25%
Folate		25%
Vitamin B12		25%
Phosphorus		15%
Magnesium		15%
Zinc 8%	●	Copper 10%

*Percent Daily Values are based on a 2,000 calorie diet. Your daily values may be higher or lower depending on your calorie needs:

		Calories: 2,000	2,500
Total Fat	Less than	65g	80g
Sat Fat	Less than	20g	25g
Cholest	Less than	300mg	300mg
Sodium	Less than	2,400mg	2,400mg
Potassium		3,500mg	3,500mg
Total Carbohydrate		300g	375g
Dietary Fiber		25g	30g

INGREDIENTS: WHEAT, MALTED BARLEY, SALT, YEAST.
VITAMINS AND MINERALS: REDUCED IRON, NIACINAMIDE, VITAMIN A PALMITATE, ZINC OXIDE (SOURCE OF ZINC), VITAMIN B6, RIBOFLAVIN (VITAMIN B2), THIAMIN MONONITRATE (VITAMIN B1), VITAMIN B12, FOLIC ACID, VITAMIN D.

1g Fat = 9 calories
1g Carbohydrate = 4 calories
1g Protein = 4 calories

Health claims and legal definitions

The new food label also provides information on those topics that reflect current health concerns, such as nutrients. The federal government has approved three health claims regarding the prevention of cancer:

a. A low fat diet may reduce your risk for cancer.

b. High fiber foods may reduce your risk for cancer.

c. Fruits and vegetables may reduce your risk for cancer.

The regulations prohibit using these claims for one nutrient if the food also contains other nutrients that undermine its benefits. While it is true that a jelly doughnut is high in fiber, it is also high in fat. Therefore, it cannot be claimed that a jelly doughnut should be part of a healthy diet.

Prior to the new labeling law, producers could use the terms "low," "high," and "free," but their meaning could vary from one product to another. Currently, these terms must meet legal definitions. If a food is described as:

- "high" in a particular nutrient, it must contain 20 percent or more of the daily value for that nutrient.
- "reduced, less, fewer," it must contain 25 percent less of a nutrient or calories.
- "fat free," it must contain only a tiny or insignificant amount of fat, less than 0.5 grams (1/8 of a teaspoon) per serving.
- "low fat," it must contain no more than 3 grams (3/4 of a teaspoon) per serving.
- "lean," it must contain less than 10 grams (2 and 1/2 teaspoons) of fat per serving and less than 4 grams (one teaspoon) of saturated fat and 95 mg of cholesterol per serving.
- "extra lean," it must contain less than 5 grams (1 and 1/4 teaspoon) of fat, 2 grams of saturated fat (1/2 teaspoon), and 95 mg of cholesterol per serving.
- "light/lite," it must contain one-third fewer calories or half the fat of the original.
- "sugar free," it must contain less than 0.5 grams per serving.
- "cholesterol free," it must contain less than 2 milligrams (mg) of cholesterol and 2 g or less of saturated fat per serving.
- "low cholesterol," it must contain 20 mg or less and 2 g or less of saturated fat per serving.

Calculation of fat, carbohydrate, and protein calories

The average daily fat consumption in the American diet is about 37% of the total caloric intake, which greatly increases the risk for chronic diseases such as cardiovascular disease, cancer, diabetes, and obesity. Less than 30% of total calories should come from fat. Of the energy nutrients carbohydrates and protein both supply the body with 4 calories per gram, while fat provides 9 calories per gram.

One way to monitor the amount of fat in your diet is to look on the food label to see how many fat grams are in a serving. As stated above, each gram of fat equals nine calories. Multiply the grams of fat by 9 and divide by the total number of calories in a serving. Multiply this number by 100 to determine the percent of calories from fat. For example, if a food label lists a total of 150 calories and 13 grams of fat, the fat content is 78% of the total calories. It is recommended that only 30% of your total daily caloric intake come from fat.

Calculation of Percent Fat Calories

Formula:
Percent of Fat Calories = (grams of fat $\times$ 9) − calories per serving $\times$ 100

Example:
One beef hot dog has:
> 13 grams of fat per serving
> 150 total calories per serving

Therefore:
> 13 grams $\times$ 9 calories per gram = 117 calories
> 117 − 150 $\times$ 100 = 78% fat*

*This means that 78% of the calories from one beef hot dog are obtained from fat.

By using this same formula you could also figure the percent of protein and carbohydrate calories provided by a certain food. By reading the label you can determine the total grams of fat, protein, or carbohydrate and substitute in the formula accordingly. Since fat provides more than twice the amount of calories per gram (9), than carbohydrate (4) and protein (4) it is recommended that you eat more carbohydrates. By using this simple formula you can decrease the amount of fat in your diet, since you will have useful information on which to base your food selections.

The Food Guide Pyramid

The food guide pyramid is a simple guideline to help you select foods for proper nutrition. Proper nutrition means that an individual's diet supplies all of the essential nutrients necessary to carry out the body's normal processes of growth, repair, and maintenance.

The amount of carbohydrates, fats, and proteins that is contained in our diet is measured in calories. A calorie is the unit of measure for the potential energy that our body can obtain from a certain amount of food. A chemical reaction must take place for a calorie of carbohydrate, fat, or protein to actually become energy.

The food guide pyramid was developed by the United States Department of Agriculture in recognition of the value that all foods have in an individual's daily diet plan. Foods are categorized into six food groups according to the nutrients they contain. Since some nutrients are needed in greater amounts than others, the number of servings from each food group will vary. The six food groups and the recommended number of servings are shown below.

Food Guide Pyramid

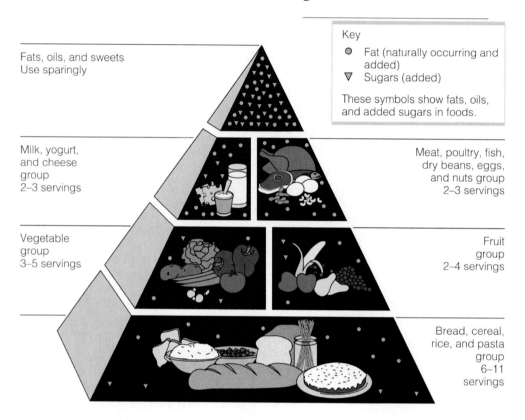

Fats, oils, and sweets
Use sparingly

Key
● Fat (naturally occurring and added)
▽ Sugars (added)

These symbols show fats, oils, and added sugars in foods.

Milk, yogurt, and cheese group
2–3 servings

Meat, poultry, fish, dry beans, eggs, and nuts group
2–3 servings

Vegetable group
3–5 servings

Fruit group
2–4 servings

Bread, cereal, rice, and pasta group
6–11 servings

Table 9–1. Sample Serving Size

Breads, cereals, rice, and pasta
1 slice of bread
½ cup of cooked rice or pasta
½ cup of cooked cereal
1 ounce of ready-to-eat cereal

Vegetables
½ cup of chopped, raw, or cooked vegetables
1 cup of leafy raw vegetables

Fruits
1 piece of fruit or melon wedge
¾ cup of juice
½ cup of canned fruit
¼ cup of dried fruit

Milk, yogurt, and cheese
1 cup of milk or yogurt
1½ to 2 ounces of cheese

Meat, poultry, fish, dry beans, eggs, and nuts
2½ to 3 ounces of cooked lean meat, poultry or fish
Count ½ cup of cooked beans, or 1 egg, or 2 tablespoons of peanut butter as 1 ounce of lean meat (about ⅓ serving)

Fats, oils, and sweets
Limit calories from these, especially if you need to lose weight

Table 9-1 provides the number of daily servings necessary to meet individual needs. Table 9-4 gives the size of a serving for a large variety of foods in each food group and their caloric content. Remember, the amount you eat at one meal may be more than one serving. For example, a dinner portion of spaghetti would count as two or three servings of pasta.

Along with exercise, eating a variety of foods based on the food guide pyramid has proven to be an effective way to assist individuals in reaching and maintaining their ideal body weight. Individuals who need to gain weight, lose weight, or are involved in an extremely vigorous exercise program, may need to modify the recommended size of each serving. Athletes may wish to add servings from the food groups that will provide additional calories of carbohydrates.

Table 9-2. Number of Servings Daily to Meet Individual Needs

	Women & some older adults	Children, teenage girls, active women, most men	Teenage boys & active men
Calorie level *	about 1,600	about 2,200	about 2,800
Bread group	6	9	11
Vegetable group	3	4	5
Fruit group	2	3	4
Milk group	**2-3	**2-3	**2-3
Meat group	2, for a total of 5 ounces	2, for a total of 6 ounces	3, for a total of 7 ounces

*These are the calorie levels if you choose low fat, lean foods from the five major food groups and use foods from the fats, oils, and sweets group sparingly.

**Women who are pregnant or breast feeding, teenagers, and young adults to age 24 need 3 servings.
Source: USDA

A closer look at fat and added sugars

The small tip of the pyramid shows fats, oils, and sweets. These are foods such as salad dressings, cream, butter, margarine, sugars, soft drinks, candies, and sweet desserts. Alcoholic beverages are also part of this group. These foods are called empty calorie foods since they provide many calories but few nutrients. Most people should go easy on foods from this group.

Some fat or sugar symbols are shown in the other food groups to remind you that some foods in these groups can also be high in fat and added sugars, such as cheese or ice cream from the milk group and french fries from the vegetable group. When choosing foods for a healthful diet, consider the fat and added sugars in your choices from all the food groups, not just fats, oils, and sweets from the pyramid tip.

Food guide pyramid food groups

Examples of foods included in each group are:

Bread, Cereal, Rice, and Pasta Group

Bread, Cereal, Rice, and Pasta Group (6–11 servings)—Enriched breads and cereals are our major energy source, since they contain large amounts of carbohydrates. This group also furnishes our body with the most fiber and provides vitamins and minerals. You need to eat more servings per day from this group than any other.

Vegetable Group

Vegetable Group (3–5 servings)—The vegetable group includes a large variety of foods from plants. Vegetables are a good source of fiber and the major source of vitamins and minerals. One serving of a dark green or deep yellow vegetable should be eaten each day, since it will provide vitamin A.

Fruit Group

Fruit Group (2–4 servings)—Fruits are a good source of fiber and a major source for vitamins and minerals. Citrus fruits provide an excellent source for vitamin C. Since vitamin C is a water soluble vitamin and cannot be stored in the body, one citrus fruit or glass of juice should be consumed daily.

Milk, Yogurt, and Cheese Group

Milk, Yogurt, and Cheese Group (2–3 servings)—Foods in this group come mostly from animals and are good sources of protein, calcium, iron, and zinc. When looking at the nutritional value of milk products, it is interesting to note the only difference between whole milk and a 2% product is the fat content. Eating low fat cheese, sour cream, and ice milk will reduce the amount of fat consumed and reduce the chances for cardiovascular diseases.

Meat, Poultry, Fish, Dry Beans, Eggs, and Nuts Group

Meat, Poultry, Fish, Dry Beans, Eggs, and Nuts Group (2–3 servings)—This food group is the major source for protein and iron, which is essential for the growth and repair of tissue, but it is also a major

161

source of fat. You should select foods from this group which have a lower fat content. For example, fish and poultry have a lower fat content than beef or pork. It is also recommended to eat small portions. Only six ounces from this group are needed daily.

Fats, Oils, and Sweets Group

Fats, Oils, and Sweets Group (sparingly) —Condiments are included in this group, such as salad dressing, butters and margarines, and a variety of cooking oils. Most of these should be used sparingly, considering both fat and sugar content. Some items in this group can be used at any time without negative health affects.

Remember, a truly balanced daily diet does not eliminate any of the first five food categories. If you are short servings from one of the food groups on a regular basis, you might not be getting an adequate amount of the nutrients supplied by that group. It is essential that we eat a variety of foods in order to obtain all of the nutrients we need.

Although the food groups included in the pyramid contain a wide variety of possibilities, many individuals fail to take advantage of the infinite options. The point to remember is you can eat a balanced diet and still make highly individual food choices.

Determining Daily Calorie Requirements

Daily calorie requirements are different for each person. How many calories a person requires to support daily body functions depend on two factors—*body mass and amount of physical activity.* The greater the body mass, the more calories required to support that body mass. The same is true for level of physical activity—the more active you are, the more calories will be required to support your body. If a construction worker and a secretary have the same size body, the construction worker will require more calories just to maintain and support daily activities.

Your body burns Calories even when you are sleeping. The amount of energy needed to maintain your body while you are sleeping is called basal metabolism.

Basal metabolism

Basal metabolism is the amount of energy required to maintain your body at rest. This rate of metabolism is known to reduce with age. Therefore, caloric intake to support basic metabolism should be reduced with age. Basal metabolism is usually estimated as one calorie per kilogram of body weight per hour. To determine basal metabolism, you must convert your body weight from pounds to kilograms. One kilogram is equal to 2.2 pounds. If John weighed 140 pounds, he would weigh 63.64 kilograms (140 divided by 2.2). John would then multiply his body weight in kilograms (63.64) by 24 hours to determine how many calories he needed to eat, just to maintain his body at rest. In John's case, this would be 1,527 additional calories (63.64 x 24) needed to maintain the basic functioning of his body, without consideration of his daily physical activity.

To determine basal metabolism requirements:

Step 1 Convert body weight to kilograms
140 (body weight) ÷ 2.2 lb/kg = 63.64 kg.
Step 2 Kilograms of body weight by 24 hours
63.64 (kg.) × 24 (hrs.) = 1,527 calories

Caloric needs for daily activities

To determine the calories required to support John's daily activities in addition to his basal metabolism, or his non-sleeping activities, he would use Table 9-3 and Table 10-1. The figures in these two tables represent the number of calories above basal metabolism required to perform certain types of daily activities, such as work and physical activities. To estimate the number of calories required to support daily activities in addition to basal metabolism, estimate the number of hours that you spend performing different types of activities included in Table 9-3 and Table 10-1. Multiply the number of hours for each type of activity by the number of calories required per hour, and then add the total number of calories for all activities. This method is further explained in Chapter 10.

Table 9–3. Energy Expenditures for Various Activities

Daily Activities	Calories Per ½ Hour	Daily Activities	Calories Per ½ Hour
Cooking	40	Making beds	60
Dressing	40	Marketing	40
Driving car	25	Mowing lawn (hand mower)	93
Dusting	40	Office work	38
Eating	15	Sawing or chopping wood	150
Gardening	68	Sitting or doing quiet seated work	15
Ironing (standing)	23	Standing	20
		Washing floor	65

Daily Diet

Your daily diet should be based on the food guide pyramid. If your daily activities include a lot of physical activities, such as athletics, you may want to add one or two servings from the bread, cereal, rice, and pasta group, a group that is high in carbohydrates. If you are very active, you may also want to add one or two servings from the fruit and the vegetable food groups. It is important to remember that when you are no longer in sports competition, you should cut back your servings, since you no longer need the extra calories.

A complete diet diary can help you evaluate your diet to see if you have a balanced diet and to determine if eating too many or too few calories.

Keep a diet log

The first step in evaluating your daily diet is to keep a daily diet log, that is, to write down everything you eat. It would also be helpful if you kept an activity log for the same time period. The best method is to keep the diet log for one week, since our lifestyles usually are very similar from week to week. If we only keep a diet log for a few days, it may indicate higher or lower caloric intake than we really have over a long period of time. As an example, if you kept your diet log only for three or four days during the week but did not include the weekend, your caloric intake might be low, since you would miss counting the pizza you had with friends over the weekend.

Once you have completed the diet log, you may now evaluate your eating patterns. For example, look to see if you included the first five food groups of the food guide pyramid and if you ate the suggested number of servings from each group. You should not be too critical of yourself if you did not meet the recommended servings each day, but over the period of a few days, you should meet the average recommendations. Next estimate the number of calories you averagely eat each day. Use Table 9–4 (table for common foods) and Table 9–5 (table on fast foods) to determine the caloric content of the foods included in your diet. Now compare your estimated daily output and your estimated daily intake. If your intake is greater, look to see where you could cut extra calories. If your output was greater, check to see if you had enough servings from the bread and cereal group, or if you were short servings from the milk group. How to adjust your diet, whether you want to gain weight or lose weight, and still maintain good nutrition will be discussed in detail in Chapter 10.

Sound nutrition contributes to a happy, active lifestyle.

Good nutrition helps you look good and feel good

Eating a diet that contains the required number of servings from the food guide pyramid, with only enough calories to maintain a desired weight, will go a long way toward giving an individual the figure or body build, complexion, or glossy hair that will make that person look good and feel good.

Table 9–4. Caloric Values of Common Foods

Bread, Cereals, Rice, and Pasta Group	Serving Size	Calories
Bagel	1 (3″)	165
Biscuit	1 (2″)	100
Bread:		
White	1 slice	70
Whole Wheat	1 slice	65
Italian	1 slice	85
Corn	1 2½″ square	160
Cereal, dry (varies with type, check label)	1 cup	90
Cooked Grain Products		
Oatmeal	½ cup	65
Grits	½ cup	65
Spaghetti	½ cup	80
Macaroni	½ cup	80
Egg Noodles	½ cup	100
Rice	½ cup	110
Crackers:		
Saltines	4	50
Graham	2 squares	55
Hush Puppies	3	150
Muffin:		
Blueberry	1 medium	110
Bran	1 medium	105
Corn	1 medium	125
Pancake	1 (4″)	60
Popcorn, popped with oil	1 cup	40
Roll:		
Hamburger/Hot Dog (1)	1	120
Submarine	1 large	390
Brown'n Serve	1	85
Waffle	1 (7″)	210

Vegetable Group	Serving Size	Calories
Beans:		
Lima	½ cup	85
Pinto	½ cup	105
Green	½ cup	15
Broccoli	½ cup	20
Cabbage	½ cup	10
Carrots:		
Raw	1 large	40
Canned	½ cup	25
Cauliflower	½ cup	15
Cole Slaw	½ cup	85
Corn	4″ ear	100
	½ cup	70
Greens:		
Collard	½ cup	30
Spinach, mustard, turnip	½ cup	20
Lettuce	1 cup	5
Mixed vegetables	½ cup	60

	Serving Size	Calories
Peas:		
Green	½ cup	75
Blackeyed	½ cup	100
Potatoes:		
Baked, no skin	1 large	140
Boiled, no skin	1 medium	70
French fries	10	110
Hash Brown	½ cup	230
Sweet:		
Baked	1 medium	160
Candied	½ medium	145
Squash:		
Summer	½ cup	15
Winter	½ cup	50
Tomato, raw	1 medium	25
Turnip	½ cup	15

Fruit Group	Serving Size	Calories
(*Unless otherwise noted, values are for raw fruits and cooked vegetables*)		
Apple	1 medium	85
Banana	1 medium	125
Grapefruit	½ medium	40
Grapes	10	35
Juices:		
Apple	8 oz.	120
Grape	8 oz.	165
Grapefruit	8 oz.	100
Lemon	1 Tbsp.	4
Orange	8 oz.	110
Orange	1 medium	65
Peach:		
Fresh	1 medium	40
Canned, heavy syrup	2 halves	80
Pear:		
Fresh	1 medium	100
Canned, heavy syrup	2 halves	75
Plum	1 small	30
Strawberries	½ cup	42
Watermelon	4″ × 8″ piece	110

Milk, Yogurt, and Cheese Group	Serving Size	Calories
Cheese:		
Cheddar	2 oz.	230
Swiss	2 oz.	210
Mozzarella, part skim	2 oz.	160
Cream	2 oz.	200
Cottage, 4% fat	1 cup	200
Cheese Pizza:		
Thin crust	¼ 13″ pie	340
Thick crust	¼ 13″ pie	390

continued

Table 9-4. Caloric Values of Common Foods, **Cont.**

Milk, Yogurt, and Cheese Group	Serving Size	Calories
Ice Cream, vanilla		
Hard	1 cup	270
Soft	1 cup	375
Milk:		
Whole	8 oz.	150
2% lowfat	8 oz.	120
2% chocolate	8 oz.	180
Skim	8 oz.	90
Buttermilk	8 oz.	90
Thick Shake:		
Vanilla	10 oz.	350
Chocolate	10 oz.	355
Yogurt:		
Plain	8 oz.	150
Vanilla, lemon	8 oz.	200
Fruit	8 oz.	260

Meat, Poultry, Fish, Dry Beans, Eggs, and Nuts Group	Serving Size	Calories
(These figures are for meat without bone)		
Bologna	2 slices	170
Chicken:		
Breast:		
Fried	½ breast	230
Broiled, no skin	3½ oz.	165
Drumstick, fried	2 small	125
Chili con carne, with beans	1 cup	340
Chuck Roast:		
With fat	3 oz.	365
Visible fat removed	3 oz.	210
Eggs:		
Boiled	1 large	80
Scrambled	1 large	110
Fish Sticks	3 oz.	150
Ham:		
With fat	3 oz.	315
Visible fat removed	3 oz.	185
Hamburger:		
21% fat	3 oz.	245
10% fat	3 oz.	185
Hot Dog	1 (2 oz.)	150
Macaroni and cheese:		
Home recipe	1 cup	430
Canned	1 cup	230
Peanut Butter	2 Tbsp.	380
Pork Chop:		
With fat	3 oz.	310
Visible fat removed	3 oz.	215
Round Steak:		
With fat	3 oz.	375
Visible fat removed	3 oz.	205
Sausage	2 small	140
Spaghetti and meat sauce	1 cup	295
Tuna Salad	½ cup	175
Turkey, light meat	3 oz.	150

Fats, Oils, and Sweets Group	Serving Size	Calories
Bacon	2 slices	85
Butter or margarine	1 Tbsp.	100
Cake:		
Angel Food, 10″	1/12 cake	160
Chocolate with icing	1/16 cake	275
Yellow with icing	1/16 cake	275
Candy:		
Chocolate	1 oz.	145
Caramel	1 oz.	115
Hershey Bar	1½ oz.	220
Snickers	2 oz.	270
Peanut M&M's	1.7 oz.	240
Peanut Butter Cups	2 large	260
Chocolate Syrup	1 Tbsp.	45
Coca Cola	12 oz.	145
Cookies:		
Chocolate Chip	1 (2¼″)	50
Oatmeal Raisin	1 (2½″)	60
Oreo	1 (1¾″)	60
Fig Newton	1	50
Brownie	1 (1¾″)	95
Granola Bar	1	120
Doughnut:		
Cake	1	100
Glazed	1	205
Ginger Ale	12 oz.	135
Honey	1 Tbsp.	60
Ice Cream Sandwich or bar	1	165
Jam	1 Tbsp.	55
Mayonnaise	1 Tbsp.	100
Nuts:		
Peanuts, roasted	¼ cup	340
Cashews	¼ cup	280
Pecans	¼ cup	205
Oil	1 Tbsp.	125
Pie:		
Apple	1/8 pie	300
Cherry	1/8 pie	310
Lemon Meringue	1/8 pie	270
Pecan	1/8 pie	430
Pumpkin	1/8 pie	240
Potato Chips	10	115
Pretzels, twisted	10	235
Pudding:		
Chocolate	1 cup	385
Vanilla	1 cup	285
Salad Dressing:		
Blue Cheese	1 Tbsp.	60
Italian	1 Tbsp.	70
Thousand Island	1 Tbsp.	80
Sour Cream	1 Tbsp.	25
Sugar	1 Tbsp.	45
Tartar Sauce	1 Tbsp.	75

continued

Table 9–4. Caloric Values of Common Foods, **Cont.**

Fats, Sweets, Alcohol Group	Serving Size	Calories	Fats, Sweets, Alcohol Group	Serving Size	Calories
Beer:			Tang	8 oz.	135
Regular	12 oz.	150	Tom Collins	10 oz.	180
Light	12 oz.	100	Wine:		
Gin, Rum, Vodka, Whiskey	1½ oz.	125	Sweet	3½ oz.	135
Hawaiian Punch	8 oz.	120	Dry		85
Kool Aid	8 oz.	100			
Lemonade	8 oz.	110			
Sprite	12 oz.	145			

From Take Control: Manage Your Weight to Look Good and Feel Great. Published by Nutrition Education and Training Program. N.C. State Dept. of Public Instruction, Healthful Living Section, Raleigh, N.C.

Table 9–5. Caloric Values of Fast Foods*

Arby's	Calories	Dairy Queen, cont.	Calories
Beef and Cheese Sandwich	450	Brazier, regular	260
Club Sandwich	560	Oyster Bar	390
Ham'n Cheese Sandwich	380	Chocolate Dipped Cone, medium	300
Junior Roast Beef Sandwich	220	Chocolate Malt, medium	600
Roast Beef Sandwich	350	Chocolate Sundae, medium	300
Super Roast Beef Sandwich	620	Float	330
Turkey Deluxe Sandwich	510	Freeze	520
Turkey Sandwich	410	Parfait	460
Burger Chef	**Calories**	Ice Cream Sandwich	140
Big Chef	542	Dilly Bar	240
Cheeseburger	304	Fiesta Sundae	570
Double Cheeseburger	434	Fish Sandwich	400
Hamburger	258	Fish Sandwich with Cheese	440
Mariner Platter	680	Hot Fudge Brownie Delight	570
Rancher Platter	640	Mr. Misty Float	440
Shake, Vanilla	326	Mr. Misty Freeze	500
Skipper's Treat	604	Super Brazier Chili Dog	555
Burger King	**Calories**	Super Brazier Dog	518
Cheeseburger	305	Super Brazier Dog with Cheese	593
French Fries	214	**Hardee's**	**Calories**
Hamburger	252	Apple Turnover	282
Hot Dog	291	Big Twin	447
Shake, Vanilla	332	Cheeseburger	335
Whaler	486	Deluxe	675
Whopper	606	Double Cheeseburger	495
Dairy Queen	**Calories**	Fish Sandwich	468
Banana Split	540	French Fries, large	381
Big Brazier, deluxe	470	French Fries, regular	239
Big Brazier, regular	457	Hamburger	305
Big Brazier with Cheese	318	Hot Dog	346
Brazier Chili Dog	330	Milkshake	391
Brazier Cheese Dog	330	Roast Beef Sandwich	390
Brazier Dog	273	**Kentucky Fried Chicken**	**Calories**
French Fries, large	320	Drumstick	136
French Fries, regular	200	Breast	283
Onion Rings	300	Rib	241

*Values are for a standard single serving size.

continued

Table 9–5. Caloric Values of Fast Foods, **Cont.**

KFC cont.	Calories
Thigh	276
Wing	151
9 Pieces Chicken	1892
Chicken Dinner, original	830
Chicken Dinner, extra crispy	950

McDonald's	Calories
Apple Pie	300
Big Mac	541
Cheeseburger	306
Cherry Pie	298
Chocolate Shake	324
Egg McMuffin	352
English Muffin, buttered	186
Fillet O'Fish	211
Hamburger	257
Hot Cakes, with butter & syrup	472
Cookies	294
Quarter Pounder with Cheese	518
Sausage	184
Scrambled Eggs	162
Strawberry Shake	345
Vanilla Shake	323

Other Mexican Foods	Calories
Enchilada:	
Beef, one	260
Beef, topped with cheese, one	340
Cheese, one	280
Guacamole, ½ cup	140
Refried Beans, ½ cup	150
Taco Salad, 1 serving	234
Tamales, one	115
Tortillas, one	40

Wendy's	Calories
Cheeseburger:	
Single with Cheese	580
Double with Cheese	800
Triple with Cheese	1040

Wendy's, cont.	Calories
Chili	230
French Fries	330
Frosty	390
Hamburger:	
Single	470
Double	670
Triple	850

Pizza Hut	Calories Thin	Thick
Standard Cheese	180	208
Standard Pepperoni	202	224
Standard Pork/Mushroom	196	227
Super Supreme	266	300
Superstyle Cheese	213	235
Superstyle Pepperoni	233	244
Superstyle Pork/Mushroom	230	244
Supreme	216	244

Ponderosa	Entree	Dinner
Baked Potato	145	
Chopped Beef	324	727
Double Deluxe	362	791
Extra-Cut Prime Rib	409	812
Extra-Cut Ribeye	358	761
Fillet of Sole Dinner	251	654
Fillet of Sole Sandwich	122	551
French Fries	230	
Junior Patty	98	446
Prime Rib	286	689
Rib Eye/Shrimp	398	801
Shrimp	220	623
Steakhouse Deluxe	181	611
Strip Sirloin	277	680
Super Sirloin	383	786
T-Bone	374	777
Tartar Sauce, 1 Tbs.	95	

*Values are for a standard single serving size.

Summary

"You are what you eat." That may be an old cliché, but in this case it is true. Teenagers and adults who look good, feel good, and lead a healthy, active, vigorous lifestyle, eat a sound nutritional diet. The nutritional habits of most people are developed from past experiences and people they have been in contact with. Many of these habits may not be the best for you. You might be able to beat the system for a while, but in the end, you will have to pay the cost for a poor diet with health problems.

Your body requires the essential nutrients to function properly and stay healthy. These nutrients include proteins, carbohydrates, fats, minerals, and vitamins. However, there are also some health concerns related to these essential nutrients, such as cholesterol and essential amino acids. So, it is not just the amount you eat of each nutrient, but the quality of what you eat.

Most healthy people can obtain the right amount of each essential nutrient by eating a balanced diet following the food guide pyramid guidelines for each of the food groups. When planning your diet, you need to consider how many calories you burn each day. There are two parts that you need to be concerned with when determining your daily requirements, basal metabolism and needs for daily activities. Some of the rewards of following a sound nutritional plan coupled with a balanced personal fitness program are plenty of energy to do all the things you want, a good feeling, improved appearance, and a positive feeling about yourself. You cannot have a complete personal fitness program unless you have a sound nutritional plan.

Study Questions

Multiple choice

Place the letter of the best answer in the space provided.

_____ 1. Generally, the strongest factor determining why teenagers eat a certain type of food is because:
   A. friends introduce us to new and different foods.
   B. of the foods we have been exposed to through travel.
   C. we are influenced by friends of different ethnic and religious backgrounds.
   D. we have been eating what our families eat since we were born.

_____ 2. Food is closely related to such health problems as:
   A. complexion.
   B. high cholesterol levels.
   C. overweight.
   D. All of the above are correct.

_____ 3. Proteins are a source of energy that:
   A. are a better source than fats.
   B. are not as good a source as carbohydrates.
   C. provide energy during strength type of activities.
   D. will be used before fats or carbohydrates.

_____ 4. The best source of energy is:
   A. amino acids.
   B. carbohydrates.
   C. fats.
   D. proteins.

_____ 5. Cholesterol is contained in:
   A. fats from olives and nuts.
   B. saturated fats.
   C. unsaturated fats.
   D. vegetable fats.

_____ 6. The type of cholesterol that is stored on the artery walls is (are):
   A. both LDL and HDL.
   B. HDL.
   C. LDL.
   D. neither HDL or LDL.

_____ 7. Minerals are often lost during food preparation because:
   A. a chemical reaction occurs when certain foods are mixed.
   B. they are only in fresh fruits and vegetables.
   C. they dissolve into the liquid and the liquid is thrown away.
   D. they dissolve when heated for a period of time.

_____ 8. Vitamins are used by the body:
   A. as a major source of energy.
   B. only in the growth process.
   C. to aid in the use of other nutrients.
   D. when there is a shortage of minerals.

_____ 9. What is the recommended minimum amount of water a person should drink each day?
   A. one quart
   B. two quarts
   C. three quarts
   D. four quarts

_____ 10. What are the six food groups of the food guide pyramid?
   A. cereal-bread, fruit, vegetable, milk, meat-poultry, fat-oils
   B. milk, meat, fruit and cereal, vegetable and bread, fat-oils
   C. milk and meat, fruit, vegetable, cereal and bread, fat-oils
   D. vegetable and cereal, fruit, bread, meat and milk, fat-oils

_____ 11. The food guide pyramid is a guideline to help insure that:
   A. body weight is maintained below national average.
   B. cholesterol content is maintained in our diet.
   C. sufficient amounts of vitamin K-9 are received.
   D. essential nutrients are not omitted from our diet.

_____ 12. The food group highest in fiber is the:
   A. bread and cereal group.
   B. vegetable group.
   C. meat and poultry group.
   D. milk and cheese group.

_____ 13. If you want to gain weight or if you are very active, you may want to increase the number of servings in the:
   A. bread and cereal group.
   B. fruit group.
   C. meat and poultry group.
   D. milk and cheese group.

_____ 14. Basal metabolism means the amount of energy required to:
   A. maintain your body are rest.
   B. maintain proper energy levels.
   C. support daily activities.
   D. support your body during exercise.

_____ 15. The purpose of keeping a daily diet log is to:
   A. determine the number of calories you are eating.
   B. determine if all food groups are represented in your diet.
   C. evaluate your eating patterns.
   D. all of the above.

Discussion

16. What are some health problems that are directly related to nutritional habits?

17. Describe how you would use a diet diary to evaluate your diet.

18. Plan a balanced diet for one day using the food guide pyramid.

19. Why are minerals and vitamins considered essential nutrients?

20. Determine the daily caloric requirements for a teenager with an active lifestyle.

BODY COMPOSITION AND WEIGHT CONTROL 10

Chapter Objectives

As you read this chapter, look for answers to these key questions:

- What are the characteristics of the three classifications of body types?

- How do you determine how much of your body weight is fat and how much is lean body mass?

- What medical problems are associated with excessive body fat?

- Why are fat children and fat teenagers more likely to be fat adults?

- What is the difference between being overweight and obese?

- What three methods could a person use to lose weight?

- Why is permanent weight control best achieved by a combination of diet and exercise?

When you have completed this chapter, you should understand the meaning of these vocabulary terms:

somatotype

endomorph

mesomorph

ectomorph

body composition

lean body mass

overweight

obese

ideal body weight

skinfold caliper

creeping obesity

anorexia nervosa

bulimia

spot reduction

Rx for Looking Good and Feeling Good

It's not what you are,

it's what you can

become.

Fredrick Hatfield

Everyone wants to be as attractive and healthy as possible. Individuals today are becoming more concerned about their physical appearance. There is a greater awareness of diet and exercise than ever before. This can be seen by the growth in such businesses as weight reduction centers, aerobic dance studios, health clubs, and an endless number of fitness and weight-control products.

The goal for many is to appear as healthy and as attractive as possible. Looking good and feeling good about yourself are important personal goals.

Body Types

It is important for you to know why you appear as you do. People have different body types due to the specific genetic makeup they inherited from their parents and grandparents. Body types describe differences in individuals beyond weight and height measurements. For example, two individuals of identical weight and height may be very different in terms of bone structure, muscle structure, and amount of body fat. Your body type is called a **somatotype.** There are three basic classifications of somatotype: *endomorph, mesomorph, and ectomorph.*

Endomorph

A large, soft, bulging body and a pear-shaped appearance characterize a pure **endomorph.** Features of this body type are:

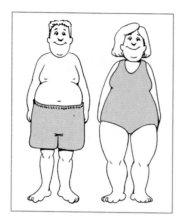

-high percentage of body fat
-short neck
-large abdomen
-wide hips
-round, full buttocks
-short, heavy legs

Mesomorph

A solid, muscular, and large-boned physique characterize a pure **mesomorph.** Features of this body type are:

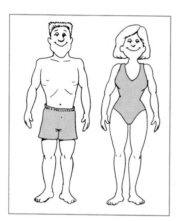

-firm, well developed muscles
-large bones
-broad shoulders
-muscular arms
-trim waist
-muscular buttocks
-powerful legs

Ectomorph

A slender body and slight build characterize a pure **ectomorph.** Features of this body type are:

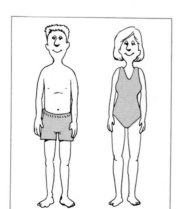

-small bones
-thin muscles
-slender arms and legs
-narrow chest
-round shoulders
-flat abdomen
-small buttocks

Very few people are pure endomorphs, mesomorphs, or ecto- morphs. Some people have characteristics of each body type. Most people are a combination of two types.

You inherit your body type from your parents and grandparents. This means you are born with a tendency toward a certain basic body type. Gaining weight will be harder for individuals with ectomorphic characteristics. Staying lean will be more difficult for individuals with endomorphic characteristics. Even though heredity influences what your body looks like, what you eat and how much you exercise play important roles in determining your body type.

Body Composition

How much you weigh is not as important as your actual body composition.

You can easily see how much you weigh by getting on a scale. But what does your weight consist of? Is it mostly muscle? Is it fat? Is it bone? Your body weight is a combination of all three. Together, muscle, bone, and fat make up what is called your **body composition.** Remember, body composition is one of the health-related compo- nents of physical fitness along with flexibility, cardiovascular fitness, muscular strength, and muscular endurance.

Lean body mass versus body fat

Lean body mass is muscle tissue and other non-fat tissue such as bones, ligaments, and tendons. Body fat results from stored calories that have not been burned up. The distribution of your lean body mass and body fat will change depending upon how active you are, how much you eat, and how fast you are growing.

Determining your body composition involves measuring your per- centage of body fat as precisely as possible. By knowing the per- centage of body fat, the percentage of lean body mass can also be determined. For example, if a person weighs 140 pounds and has 20 percent body fat, then 28 pounds of his or her weight is fat (140 lbs. $\times$ 20% = 28 lbs.). The other 80 percent, or 112 pounds, is lean body mass.

Height and weight charts can be misleading

People review standard height and weight charts to see how much they should weigh. The ranges on height and weight charts represent average weights and can be misleading. They do not tell you how much of your weight is lean body mass and how much is body fat. For example, a person who does not exercise regularly could be in the acceptable range according to a height and weight chart, but have excessive fat. On the other hand, a muscular person might be con- sidered overweight according to a height and weight chart, yet have very little body fat. A point to remember is that muscle mass weighs more and takes up less space than the same amount of fat tissue.

According to height and weight charts:

This person is overweight.

This person's weight is normal.

Many people have the mistaken belief that their body weight is the most crucial thing. How much you weigh is not as important as your actual body composition. Weighing yourself cannot be used to determine your percentage of body fat and lean body mass. Therefore, it is important for you periodically to measure your body fat and to make sure that most of the weight you are gaining is lean body mass.

Overweight versus obese

Overweight and obese are words often used interchangeably. However, they do not mean the same thing. In order to obtain your proper or ideal body weight, it is important you understand the meanings of these terms.

Overweight people are those who exceed their desirable body weight by 10 percent, according to height and weight charts. Remember, height and weight charts do not tell you how much of your body weight is fat. You can be overweight on height and weight charts and still have an acceptable level of body fat. Remember, muscle weighs more than body fat and takes up less space.

Obese people are those who have an excessive amount of body fat. You can be obese without being overweight. It is not so much a question of how heavy you are, but how much excess body fat you have that is important to your health and appearance.

Ideal body weight

Ideal body weight means how much you would weigh if you had an appropriate percentage of body fat. It has also been described as the weight at which you look good and feel the most comfortable. It is the healthiest weight for your body.

The correct or ideal percentage of body fat will vary with age and sex. The chart below illustrates acceptable ranges of body fat. A person should try to stay below the upper limits given. A person at the lower limit would be described as lean.

Age	Males	Females
up to 30	9%–15%	14%–21%
30–50	11%–17%	15%–23%
50 and up	12%–19%	16%–25%

As you can see, the ideal weight for your body is an individual and personal matter. There is no single ideal body weight for people with the same body size and shape. For example, an athlete may weigh more than others of his age and height, but the extra weight is in the form of muscle, not fat. On the other hand, a person who does very little exercise may weigh as much as the athlete, but have too much body fat.

Methods of Measuring Body Fat

Four methods are commonly used for measuring body fat: *underwater weighing, analysis by electrical impedance, skinfold measurements, and measurements of body circumference.* Underwater weighing is the most accurate means for measuring body fat. However, it requires specialized, costly equipment and highly trained individuals to operate the equipment.

Underwater weighing

Underwater weighing is the most accurate means for testing body fat. This method requires a large water tank or swimming pool and a weighing scale. The scale is used for weighing the person in air and then for weighing the person underwater.

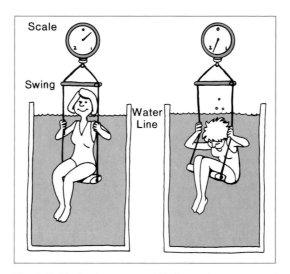

The individual submerges totally for underwater weighing.

Electrical impedance

Analysis by electrical impedance utilizes a computer-like analyzer to determine percentage of body fat. Electrodes are placed on the right hand and right foot, while the person is lying down. A harmless electrical current is transmitted instantaneously from electrode to electrode. The resistance to the electrical current is related to total body water. Calculations using total body water and lean body mass provide your percentage of body fat.

Skinfold measurements

Another method for assessing body fat is with skinfold measurements. This technique utilizes an instrument called a **skinfold caliper** to measure a fold of skin and its underlying layer of fat at key locations on the body. Approximately half of your body fat is located deep within your body. The other half is found underneath your skin between the skin and muscles. The diagram below shows how a skinfold caliper measures the thickness of a fold of skin and its underlying layer of fat. Special computations provide your percentage of body fat based on the various measurements of skinfold thickness.

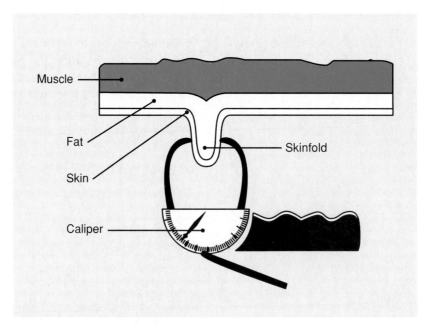

Drawing illustrates location of fat under the skin and how a caliper is used to measure the thickness of a skinfold.

Body circumference measurement

The least accurate, method for determining percentage of body fat is the measurement of body circumference. This method uses the circumference of selected body parts plus your weight. A cloth measuring tape and a scale are the only equipment needed for this method. Special computations provide your percentage of body fat.

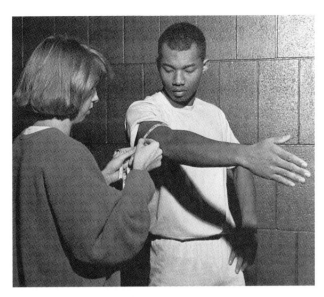

Measuring the circumference of selected body parts

Importance of Weight Control

Weight control is a major health problem in the United States. It is estimated that more than half the adults in this country are overweight. Research has found American youth to be fatter than they have been at any time in the past thirty years. It is believed that this is due to a higher standard of living, increased mechanization, more leisure time, less physical activity, insufficient knowledge about weight control, and a lack of motivation toward weight control.

Excess fat is unhealthy

Though some body fat is necessary, it is now an accepted medical fact that excess fat is bad for your health. Research shows that American men who are obese have a life expectancy that is 20 percent shorter than men of average weight. Obese women have a life expectancy that is 10 percent shorter than women of average weight. People with excessive fat have a higher risk of developing medical problems. Health hazards from excessive fat include:

breathing difficulties	kidney disorders
diabetes	surgical risk
cancer	pregnancy problems
high blood pressure	less resistance to infections
heart disease	shortened life expectancy
stroke	social discrimination

Excess body fat is not only unhealthy, it will also keep you from looking, feeling, and performing as well as you could. Feeling good about your weight and understanding how to obtain and maintain your proper or ideal body weight are important goals for everyone interested in personal fitness.

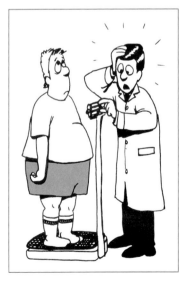

Weight control is a major health problem.

Vulnerable stages for fat cell growth

There are three major time periods in your life when fat cells are primarily formed: (a) during the last month of fetal development, (b) during the first year of life, and (c) during the growth spurt of adolescence. Your total number of fat cells becomes permanently established once you reach adulthood.

limit fat cells now

When adolescents and children grow fatter, both an increase in the size of existing fat cells and an increase in the number of fat cells occur. When adults grow fatter, only an increase in the size of existing fat cells occurs.

Fat children and fat teenagers are more likely to be fat adults because they developed more fat cells. These extra fat cells make it easier to get fatter. Weight control is more difficult for individuals who have extra fat cells. However, with adequate exercise and proper diet, people with extra fat cells can achieve and maintain their ideal body weight.

creeping obesity

As people reach adulthood, they usually start to gain weight. Excess calories add up day by day, month by month, and year by year. People do not become overweight or obese overnight, but over a period of time. The slow gaining of fat over a period of years is called **creeping obesity.**

An excess of ten calories per day beyond what you need over a year results in one additional pound of fat. After ten years you will have gained ten pounds and will begin to experience what is referred to as middle-age spread. Maybe you have noticed this is occurring in your parents or their friends. If there is an excess of 100 calories (one slice of bread) per day for one year, the weight gain is ten pounds. This translates to one dress size larger for women. Over a five-year period, the dress size creeps from a size 6 to a size 14.

The average weight gain for Americans between the ages of 25 and 55 is 30 pounds. Since an increase in age is usually accompanied by a decrease in the basal metabolic rate and a decrease in physical activity, the weight gained is more likely fat tissue than muscle tissue.

Creeping obesity does not have to happen. You can maintain your ideal body weight throughout your life by exercising regularly and eating a proper diet.

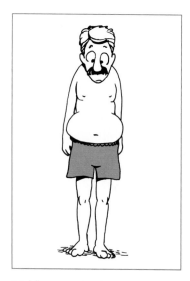

Middle-age spread

Weight Loss, Weight Gain, and Weight Maintenance

Recall that a calorie is a measure of energy the body is able to produce from food. Each pound of weight is equivalent to approximately 3,500 calories. To gain a pound, you must take in and store 3,500 calories. To lose a pound, you must burn off that amount of calories.

To reach your ideal body weight, you must balance what you eat (caloric intake) against what your body uses (caloric output). Weight loss or weight gain can be achieved by (1) changing caloric intake, (2) changing caloric output, or (3) a combination of the two.

Weight loss

You must unbalance your caloric intake or output to have a weight loss. To lose a pound a week (1 pound = 3,500 Calories), you could do one of the following:

1. Eat 500 calories less each day than your average daily caloric output.
2. Add exercise each day in an amount that would be equal to burning 500 calories.
3. Do a combination of the two, such as eating 250 calories less and engaging in exercise that would be equal to burning 250 calories.

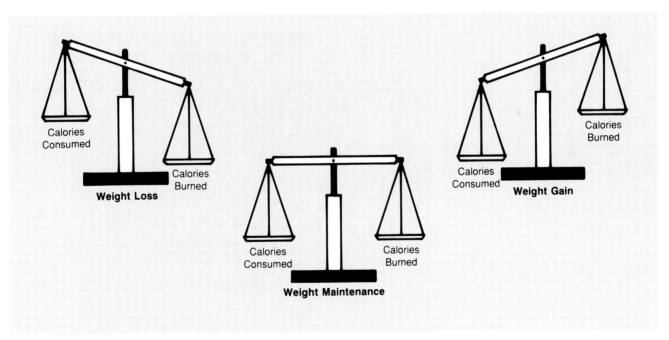

To have a weight loss or weight gain you must unbalance your caloric intake or output. To maintain weight you must balance your caloric intake and output.

Weight gain

You must also unbalance your caloric intake or output to gain weight. To gain a pound a week (1 pound = 3,500 calories), you could do one of the following:

1. Eat 500 calories more each day than your average daily caloric output.

2. Reduce your exercise each day by the amount that would be equal to burning 500 calories.

3. Do a combination of the two, such as eating 250 calories more and reducing your exercise by the amount that would be equal to burning 250 calories.

Weight maintenance

To maintain weight, your caloric intake should be the same as your average daily caloric output. In other words, you have to consume as many calories as your body burns.

Caloric Cost of Physical Activities

You use up calories when you exercise. How many calories you use during any activity depends upon the intensity at which you perform the activity, the length of time you participate, your skill level, and your body weight.

The approximate caloric cost of various activities is shown in the Estimated Caloric Cost of Selected Activities Chart. The left hand column provides an estimate of the number of calories burned per minute per pound of body weight. The three weight classification examples provide an estimate of the number of calories burned in the various activities during a 30-minute period.

Number of calories burned depends on a number of factors.

To calculate the caloric cost for a given activity, take the calories burned per minute per pound and multiply by your weight and the number of minutes the activity is performed. For example, a 120-pound individual running at a rate of six miles per hour (10 minutes/mile) would burn 284 calories during a 30-minute period.

$$0.079 \times 120 \times 30 = 284$$

| calories/minute/pound | weight | minutes | calories |

The best kinds of activities for losing weight are those that burn the most calories per minute. Such activities include bicycling, running, swimming, basketball, soccer, handball, paddleball, and cross country skiing.

Table 10-1. Estimated Caloric Cost of Selected Activities

The left hand column provides an estimate of the number of calories burned per minute per pound of body weight for selected activities. The three weight classification examples provide an estimate of the number of calories burned in the various activities during a 30-minute period.

Activity	Cal/min/lb	100 lb	140 lb	180 lb
Archery	.034	102	143	184
Badminton:				
moderate	.039	117	164	211
vigorous	.065	195	273	351
Baseball:				
infield/outfield	.031	93	130	167
pitching	.039	117	164	211
Basketball:				
moderate	.047	141	197	254
vigorous	.066	198	277	356
Bicycling:				
slow (5 mph)	.025	75	105	135
moderate (10 mph)	.05	150	210	270
fast (13 mph)	.072	216	302	389
Bowling	.028	84	118	151
Calisthenics	.045	135	189	243
Canoeing:				
2.5 mph	.023	69	97	124
4.0 mph	.047	141	197	254
Dancing:				
slow	.029	87	122	157
moderate	.045	135	189	243
fast	.064	192	269	346
Fencing:				
moderate	.033	99	139	178
vigorous	.057	171	239	308
Fishing	.016	48	67	86
Football (tag)	.04	120	168	216
Golf	.029	87	122	157
Gymnastics:				
light	.022	66	92	119
heavy	.056	168	235	302
Handball	.063	189	265	340
Hiking	.042	126	176	227
Hill Climbing	.06	180	252	324
Horseback Riding:				
walk	.019	57	80	103
trot	.046	138	193	248
gallop	.067	201	281	362

continued

Table 10–1. Estimated Caloric Cost of Selected Activities,
continued

The left hand column provides an estimate of the number of calories burned per minute per pound of body weight for selected activities. The three weight classification examples provide an estimate of the number of calories burned in the various activities during a 30-minute period.

Activity	Cal/min/lb	100 lb	140 lb	180 lb
Jogging:				
4.5 mph (13:30 min/mi)	.063	189	265	340
Judo	.087	261	365	470
Karate	.087	261	365	470
Mountain Climbing	.086	258	361	464
Paddleball	.069	207	290	373
Rowing:				
moderate (2.5 mph)	.036	108	151	194
vigorous	.118	354	496	637
Running:				
6 mph (10 min/mi)	.079	237	332	427
10 mph (6 min/mi)	.1	300	420	540
Sailing	.02	60	84	180
Skating:				
moderate	.036	108	151	194
vigorous	.064	192	269	346
Skiing (snow):				
downhill	.059	177	248	319
cross country	.078	234	328	421
Soccer	.063	189	265	340
Squash	.07	210	294	378
Stationary Running:				
70–80 counts/min	.078	234	328	421
Swimming (crawl)				
20 yards/min.	.032	96	134	173
45 yards/min.	.058	174	244	313
50 yards/min.	.071	213	298	383
Table Tennis:				
moderate	.026	78	109	140
vigorous	.04	120	168	216
Tennis:				
moderate	.046	138	193	248
vigorous	.06	180	252	324
Volleyball:				
moderate	.036	108	151	194
vigorous	.065	195	273	351
Walking:				
slow	.023	69	97	124
moderate	.032	96	134	173
fast	.044	132	185	208
Water Skiing	.053	159	223	286
Weight Training	.05	150	210	270
Wrestling	.091	273	382	491

Permanent Weight Control Methods

Achieving and maintaining your ideal body weight can be realized through three methods: (1) diet, (2) exercise, or (3) a combination of diet and exercise. The combination of exercise and proper diet is the best way to achieve and maintain your ideal body weight. One advantage of the combined method is that neither food reduction nor the increase in exercise needs to be as severe as if either were practiced alone. Another advantage is that weight loss is mostly fat, not lean tissue. However, this is not true when you attempt a weight-reduction program by dieting without exercise. When you lose weight by this method, lean tissue is lost along with fat. Dieting alone also slows down your metabolism, which makes fat loss more difficult and can cause fatigue. Exercise speeds up metabolism, burns calories, and decreases body fat. Another important advantage of combining diet and exercise is the improvement of flexibility, cardiovascular fitness, muscular strength, and muscular endurance.

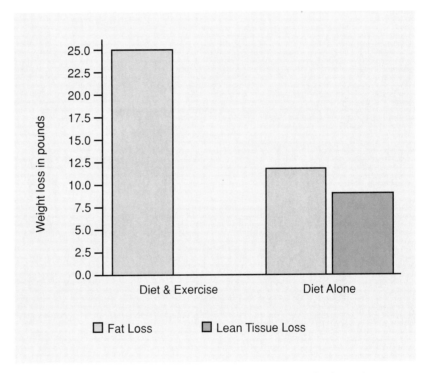

A combination of dieting and exercise will cause more fat to be lost. Dieting alone will result in a loss of lean tissue, as well as fat.

Eating smart

Eating smart is important to achieving and maintaining your ideal body weight. Smart eating habits will help you look good and feel good, have plenty of energy for schoolwork and other activities you enjoy, and maintain a healthy body for now and in the future.

Eating smart is not difficult. It simply means being knowledgeable about how much and what kinds of food you eat. The following are recommendations for eating smart:

1. Increase your consumption of fruits, vegetables, pastas, breads, unsweetened cereals, and grains such as barley, wheat, oats, cornmeal, and rice.

2. Reduce your consumption of red meats such as beef, pork, and lamb.

3. Increase your consumption of chicken, turkey, and fish.

Instead of…	Try…
Fried Chicken Breast With Skin	Baked Chicken Breast Without Skin
French Fries (6 oz)	Baked Potato With Margarine (1 pat)
Cole Slaw (3 oz)	Cooked Carrots (3 oz)
Whole Milk (1 cup)	Skim Milk (1 cup)
Vanilla Ice Cream (4 oz)	Vanilla Non-Fat Frozen Yogurt (4 oz)
Total Calories: 1079 Fat: 49 gm* Saturated Fat: 20 gm Cholesterol: 241 mg *41% calories from fat	Total Calories: 760 Fat: 10 gm* Saturated Fat: 2 gm Cholesterol: 150 mg *12% calories from fat

Eat smart! Build a better meal.

4. Eat foods that are broiled or baked rather than fried. Frying doubles the number of calories in foods. A broiled chicken leg has 45 calories and a fried chicken leg has 90.

5. Reduce your consumption of high-fat foods such as eggs, butter, whole milk, ice cream, all fried foods, and whole-milk cheeses.

6. Reduce your consumption of high-cholesterol foods such as bacon, sour cream, hot dogs, hamburgers, luncheon meats, and gravies.

7. Reduce your consumption of foods containing a lot of sugar such as pastries, candies, sweetened drinks, honey, jams, jellies, syrups, most sweet desserts, and sweetened cereals.

8. Reduce your consumption of table salt and foods high in salt such as potato chips, crackers, condiments, pickles, and canned fish.

These guidelines do not mean you should never eat a hamburger or French fries. These recommendations should be used as a guide to help you become more aware of what foods you eat.

Eating smart also means looking at your diet as a giant balance sheet. When you eat foods that may not be good for you, balance your diet with foods that are nutritionally better. For example, if you eat bacon and eggs for breakfast, eat a fruit salad for lunch.

Long-haul concept

Weight loss is usually longer lasting if it is gradual. It is recommended that you lose no more than one to two pounds per week. This is called the long-haul approach to weight reduction.

Being overweight is not the problem. Bad habits that lead to being overweight are the problem. It is important that you develop proper eating and exercise habits, which will help ensure that you keep the weight off once your ideal body weight is reached. Your goal should be to get it off and keep it off, using the long-haul concept. Or better still, never put on the extra weight. Most people look their best and feel their best both physically and mentally when they maintain their ideal body weight.

The following behavioral changes may be of benefit if you are trying to lose or maintain your weight:

1. Keep a record of what, when, and where you eat. Look for patterns of bad habits, such as eating candy when you are upset. You are more likely to be successful if you try to modify one bad habit at a time, rather than tackling two or three.

2. Avoid eating while reading or watching television. A complete bag of chips could be consumed before you know it.

3. When eating snacks, do not eat out of the bag. Rather, pour out a small amount into a bowl. Remember, ten chips are equal to 100 calories.

4. Eat breakfast every day. Those who skip this meal usually snack before lunch, eating less nutritious food and more calories than if they had eaten breakfast.

5. Drink a glass of water before you sit down for a meal. The water will help your stomach feel fuller.

6. Eat slowly by chewing your food well. If you have eaten small portions and are still hungry, wait twenty minutes. It takes this long for the stomach to transmit a signal to the brain that it is full.

Some habits, such as chewing your foods slowly, will help you lose weight.

Eating Disorders

Unfortunately, some people become so obsessed with the fear of being overweight that they refuse to eat normally. This disorder is called **anorexia nervosa.** Anorexics have distorted body images. Sometimes they look like walking skeletons. People suffering from anorexia nervosa can starve to death or die from severe vitamin and mineral deficiencies.

Another eating disorder is **bulimia.** Bulimics use laxatives and self-induced vomiting to avoid gaining weight. They frequently eat too much food, then get rid of it by inducing vomiting, using laxatives, and exercising very strenuously. These repeated actions can cause serious medical problems.

Anorexia nervosa and bulimia are very serious eating disorders. People suffering from these disorders need both medical and psychological help to overcome their disease. If you know someone who has one of these disorders, encourage them to seek help.

Weight Control Misconceptions

Because of the emphasis placed on weight control in our society, some misconceptions have developed about exercise and weight control. The following misconceptions are most common among teenagers.

Exercise and fat loss

Some people believe that participating in physical activity will not help you lose weight because of the time it takes to burn 3,500 calories through exercise. This myth comes from those who say it takes 8½ hours of playing tennis, 11½ hours of walking, or 7 hours of splitting wood to lose one pound of fat. The impression is that such exercise has to be done during one long session. You cannot lose a large amount of weight quickly by exercising. You can lose fat over the long haul by exercising regularly. Jogging for twenty minutes a day, seven days a week, over a one-year period will allow you to shed more than 20 pounds.

You cannot lose weight overnight by exercising during one long session.

Spot reduction

There is a widely held myth that exercising the muscles in a particular area of the body will remove fat from that area. This is called **spot reduction.** There is no such thing as spot reduction. Exercising will only tone-up or strenghten the muscles in a specific area.

Increased appetite

Another myth is that an increase in physical activity automatically creates an increase in appetite. Mild to moderate exercise will in fact decrease the appetite for most people.

Glandular problems

A popular myth is that excessive fat is caused by glandular problems. In reality, only a small percentage of people have glandular problems that make it difficult to control fat.

Summary

Heredity plays a role in your physical appearance. Your genetic makeup determines your body type. There are three basic classifications of body type: endomorph (stocky), mesomorph (muscular), and ectomorph (thin).

Body weight is made up of body fluids, lean body mass, and body fat. This is called body composition. Height and weight charts can be misleading because they do not indicate how much of your body weight is lean body mass and how much is body fat.

Weight gain is not always bad. Excessive fat is what should be avoided. Several methods are used for determining the percentage of body fat. Measurements taken with a skinfold caliper are reliable and easy to use. An acceptable percentage of body fat for the average person your age is 9 to 15 percent for males and 14 to 21 percent for females.

Weight control is a major health problem. Fat children and fat teenagers are more likely to become fat adults. Excessive body fat can contribute to a number of health problems, including high blood pressure, heart disease, stroke, diabetes, and kidney disorders, as well as reduced self-image.

Weight loss or gain can be achieved by (1) changing caloric intake, (2) changing caloric output, or (3) a combination of the two. To maintain weight, your caloric intake (what you take in) should be the same as your average daily caloric output (what you burn up). Permanent weight control is best achieved by a combined program of proper nutrition and regular exercise.

Study Questions

Vocabulary matching

Place the letter of the correct answer in the space provided.

_____ 1. Creeping obesity

_____ 2. Lean body mass

_____ 3. Obese

_____ 4. Somatotypes

_____ 5. Overweight

_____ 6. Bulimia

_____ 7. Long-haul concept

_____ 8. Ideal body weight

_____ 9. Anorexia nervosa

_____ 10. Skinfold caliper

A. Excessive accumulation of body fat

B. Muscle tissue, bones, ligaments, and tendons

C. Exceeds desirable body weight by 10 percent according to height and weight charts

D. Gaining fat very slowly over a period of years

E. Slow, gradual weight reduction

F. Physical classifications of the human body

G. Self-imposed state characterized by severe weight loss

H. Disease in which one eats excessively, then induces vomiting

I. Your weight with an acceptable percentage of body fat

J. An instrument used to measure amount of body fat

True–false

Circle "T" for all correct statements and "F" for all incorrect ones.

T F 11. A square body with hard, rugged, prominent muscles best describes a pure ectomorph.

T F 12. Staying lean will be more difficult for individuals with endomorphic characteristics.

T F 13. How much you weigh is as important as your actual body composition.

T F 14. An acceptable percentage of body fat for teenagers is 9–15 percent for males and 14–21 percent for females.

T F 15. The most accurate method for testing body fat is with a skinfold caliper.

T F 16. There is a close association between overweight people and heart disease.

T F 17. Body fat weighs more than an equal amount of lean body mass.

T F 18. Fat children and fat teenagers are more likely to be fat adults.

T F 19. Anorexia nervosa is a disease in which the individual eats excessively, then induces vomiting.

T F 20. Increased exercise is usually followed by an increase in appetite.

Discussion

21. Why are height and weight charts not very useful standards?

22. What is the difference between actual body weight and ideal body weight?

23. Explain why many adults and youth in the United States are over-weight.

24. Explain how you would lose weight, gain weight, and maintain your weight.

25. Why is the combination of sound nutrition and regular exercise the most desirable method for permanent weight control?

STRESS 11

Chapter Objectives

As you read this chapter, look for answers to these key questions:

- What is stress and why do some of your peers react differently to a specific situation than you?

- What are the common causes of stress?

- What are the effects of stress on the body?

- How do positive stress and negative stress affect you as an individual?

- What are the components of a stress management program?

- What are stress diversion activities and how are they helpful?

- What are negative coping techniques and why should you avoid them?

When you have completed this chapter, you should understand the meaning of these vocabulary terms:

stress	stimulus
positive stress (eustress)	adrenaline
negative stress (distress)	time management
stressor	stress diversion activities
homeostasis	positive coping strategies
fight or flight response	negative coping techniques
general adaptation syndrome	

Case Study: Sammy's Story

Most people are about as happy as they make up their minds to be.

Abraham Lincoln

The school year was only two weeks old, but Sammy was already frustrated, confused, and lost. He felt like he was *drowning.* Sammy was in the ninth grade at Midway High School, and he didn't know anyone. During the summer, he and his family had moved to Midway from a smaller town. The middle school he had attended last year was small, and Sammy knew all of the students and teachers. He received personal attention in his classes which enabled him to do well and receive excellent grades. He was also active in after-school activities, and was particularly a standout in athletics.

Many teenagers will feel a great deal of loneliness, even in a crowd, like at school. This is especially true when you are placed in a new situation.

During these first two weeks at Midway High, Sammy had not found or experienced any of the positive things that made him enjoy school in the past. The teachers had large classes and were too busy to give students individual attention. The football coach had discouraged him from coming out for the team because he was *too small, didn't know the system,* and would have trouble adjusting.

Sammy did not know anyone, and no one knew him. The school was very large, very crowded, and it seemed to Sammy, very noisy. To Sammy, it seemed all of the other students had their own peer group with no room for new people. Students smoked openly at Midway,

199

popped pills, and drank alcohol. Sammy thought half of the students spent most of the time high on one thing or another. In fact, these were the only students who had shown any interest in him and had freely offered him different types of drugs. Although he had always turned them down, he found himself thinking that if he accepted their offer just once, maybe he would make friends and be accepted. But that thought scared him; could he accept only once?

Sammy's feelings of loneliness in his new school are common. We all need friends to talk to and share with.

At home, Sammy's family was just as confusing. Everyone had their own problems adjusting to new jobs, new friends, new everything. There did not seem to be the time or the interest to listen to Sammy's problems at school. His mother had passed it off as a period of adjustment. Sammy felt himself withdrawing. He was floating through school, and at the end of the day he could not remember any details. He only remembered an increasingly desperate feeling.

What's wrong with Sammy?

Sammy is experiencing stress from many sources. He does not understand what is happening to him. He has never heard of stress or the causes of stress. He does not know what coping strategies (techniques of dealing with stress) are or how to use them. If Sammy does not receive help with his stress soon, it is likely he will begin protecting himself by using whatever means are easiest or available to him. Withdrawal, negative behavior, and drug abuse are all unconscious, and unfortunately common, reactions to stress. Sammy's new life has him in a "pressure cooker" and the pressure is building. Sammy needs help or the pressure will build to a point of explosion. The help Sammy

When we feel alone, we will often accept the friendship of anyone who offers it. We should be careful that we do not choose a group of friends who have a set of values that are not acceptable.

needs may be the friendship of people, or it may be in the form of knowledge about what is happening to him and how he can deal with it in a positive manner.

What Is Stress?

Stress is the nonspecific response of the body to any demand made upon it and may vary from one individual to another. It may be caused by both good things (a good grade on a test) and bad things (getting cut from the team). Therefore, stress can be either *good* or *bad,* depending on how you and your body react to the specific demand.

If stress results from something good and you react to it in a positive manner, the stress is good. Good stress, or positive stress, is called **eustress.** If stress is caused by something bad or if you react to a given situation in a negative manner, the stress will be bad for you. Bad stress, or negative stress, is called **distress.**

Individuals react differently to stress

Different people react to the same demand differently. Some people may receive negative stress when the teacher calls on them in class, while others receive positive stress from having the opportunity to answer questions in class. Therefore, you can see that stress is specific to each individual. How you react to a specific demand may be completely different from the reaction of any of your friends or classmates. This does not mean you have a problem or that you are abnormal. It just means that you are an individual, and that is good.

The importance of understanding stress

It is not unusual that Sammy did not understand what was happening to him. He did not know about stress and its causes, or how to deal with new or different sources of stress. Most people, adults as well as teenagers, do not understand or are not even aware of stress and the consequences of too much negative stress. Many people who are aware of stress think of it only as negative. If teenagers and parents understood stress, they could help each other. They would better understand why someone reacts in a certain way and generally could help each other develop a better lifestyle.

What Causes Stress?

Things that cause stress are referred to as **stressors.** Nearly everything is a stressor, creating either positive stress (eustress) or negative stress (distress). Every activity encountered will stress you, with each activity creating a different degree of stress. Some of these activities will cause you negative stress, and some will cause you positive stress. Remember, when you experience positive stress, your best friend may experience negative stress from the same activity because you are different individuals.

Extreme heat and cold temperatures cause the **homeostasis** (internal balance) of your body to be upset. This is a negative physical stressor that requires a physical response. However, these extreme temperatures can also cause mental stress.

The death of a person who is close to you will require both a physical and a mental response. The death of a family member may even be a positive stressor. For example, this might happen when the person has been ill for a long time.

Potential causes of stress

You have many potential sources of stress that may be bombarding you everyday. These may include family relationships, school work, peer groups, discrimination, injury, sickness, or fatigue. These stressors can generate both positive stress and negative stress. How you handle or react to these stressors will determine their effect on you and your lifestyle.

Are all changes stressors?

Yes, even those changes in your daily routine that are pleasant and make you happy cause stress. This type of stressor would not cause as great a stress as a change that was bad, but the body would still need to make an adjustment and use up some of your energy reserve. An example of this is a summer vacation or a holiday season. Many people feel physically tired at the end of their vacation, even though it was enjoyable. This fatigue is caused by the body using up its energy reserve to make all of the adjustments to changes in its normal routine. A good change, such as a vacation, does not create as much negative stress as a bad change (death in family, divorce). But if you are not aware that the situation is stressful, you may let it negatively affect you and ruin your family's vacation.

Major stressors come in many forms

Major changes in your life are the real negative stressors for which you need to plan coping techniques in order to handle them positively. Sammy's family moved, a change that frequently creates a great deal of negative stress in all family members. This is true even if such a move or change is caused by something positive (a promotion within the company that requires a parent to move to another city, or being hired by another company at a much higher salary).

Moving from one community or town to another is a major change and usually causes all members in the family a great deal of negative stress, even if the long-term results may be positive.

If a family, like Sammy's, is required to move, an adjustment in the behavior of all family members should be expected. This change in behavior occurs even though the move is due to a positive reason. If the move is regarded as a negative situation, the emotional response will be even greater. Children often think a family move is negative because they are going to move away from friends and a comfortable, secure environment. Although family members are expected to act in a calm, mature manner, they may in fact feel anger and resentment toward other members of the family or employers. In such a situation, children frequently let resentment against their parents build.

If the threat of stress caused by the move is managed in an appropriate manner, the resulting response will be positive rather than negative. But if you find no satisfactory way to cope with the stress, you will feel increasingly angry and resentful. This continued buildup of stress will cause a weakening of the body systems.

How Does Your Body React to Stress?

Your body responds physiologically in *exactly* the same manner to both positive and negative stress. The body's response to a specific stressor will occur in a sequence of three steps, or stages. This sequence is known as the *general adaptation syndrome*. The first stage is the *alarm phase*. The body makes an immediate response to a stressor, anticipating change, and perceiving change as a danger or an emergency. During the second stage, the body learns, or tries to learn, to adapt to the stressor, or it goes through a *stage of resistance*. The third stage, *exhaustion*, occurs when the body uses up the energy reserves required for coping with stress.

Fight or flight response

Initiation of the alarm phase occurs when the body receives a *stimulus* (a signal such as one of your parents yelling at you for not carrying out the garbage). This stimulus immediately activates the nervous system which releases adrenaline into the body. **Adrenaline** is the chemical which gives you energy to perform physical acts in an emergency. By increasing the supply of adrenaline, the body moves into the fight or flight mode. The **fight or flight response** is your body's natural protective technique. Every single stressor causes the same thing to happen in your body whether it is a positive stressor or a negative stressor. The amount of adrenaline released depends on the strength of the stimuli and your previous experience with that stressor.

Hearing
Muscle Tension
Blood Pressure
Adrenaline Secretion

Pupil Dilation
Respiration
Heart Rate
Blood Sugar
Digestion

Glycogen + Fat _____ Energy

The ''Fight or Flight'' response causes many changes to occur in the body. These changes are the same for both positive and negative stress.

The release of additional adrenaline causes body functions to change. The more important changes include:

1. Blood circulation increases to provide your brain, lungs, and muscles with more nutrients (fuel for energy).

2. Nutrients (energy supplies) in the blood increase.

3. Muscles are strengthened to respond to the "fight or flight" mode.

4. Breathing becomes more rapid to give you more oxygen.

5. Your senses become more alert (the pupils of your eyes dilate to sharpen vision).

How does your mind react to stress?

You respond to stress both physically and mentally. Your mental response usually involves such emotions as happiness, joy, fear, and anger. The mental or emotional changes you exhibit in response to a stressor will actually control how you respond physically. If the emotions caused by the stressor are strong enough, you will undergo a change in behavior.

The psychological (*mental*) changes in behavior that occur due to an emotional response to stress can be classified into four areas:

1. Rationalizing: Making up reasons why things turned out the way they did, rather than the way they should have.

2. Projecting: Blaming someone else for your own faults.

3. Compensation: Over-reacting to make up for a feeling of inadequacy.

4. Avoidance: Refusing to act on a situation.

Although common, these forms of behavior are not considered healthy and, if not corrected, can lead to more serious mental disturbances.

Permitting yourself to practice these mental responses to negative stress will lead you to more serious problems.

How Does Stress Affect You?

As was mentioned on the previous pages, stress has both positive and negative effects. The manner in which you respond to the stress, both physically and mentally, will determine if the immediate and long-term effects of stress are positive or negative.

The degree to which stress affects you physically is also determined by what you are doing when you receive the stimuli from a stressor and additional adrenaline is released. If you are physically active when the adrenaline is released, it will be easier for you to deal with the stress because the exercise will burn up the additional supply of adrenaline and will allow body functions (such as heart rate and blood pressure) to return to normal. This will not happen if you are sitting. When sitting, the body reacts to the stressor in the very same manner that it would if you were active, except the adrenaline is not burned up quickly. The adrenaline will remain in the body system for a long period of time, keeping body functions at an unusually high level. If your blood pressure is frequently elevated by stress and not subsequently lowered by exercise, you could develop high blood pressure.

Positive stress (eustress)

Stress affects you in a positive manner every day. It can provide you with the energy and motivation to accomplish things you want to do or that have been demanded of you. Positive stress will make you more creative, alert, aggressive, and dedicated to a task. Positive stress will keep you from becoming bored and fatigued with your daily tasks. By helping you resist fatigue and boredom, positive stress will make you feel good about yourself. You will be alert and happier. You will not be nervous or uptight, but relaxed and easy going. Your peers will view you as if you are feeling good about yourself.

Physical activity will help burn up adrenalin that is released in a stressful situation.

Negative stress (distress)

Too much stress can have a negative affect and can interfere with school work, homelife, and how you relate to your peers. It can even lead to health problems over an extended period of time. The effects of negative stress can pile up on you. They act on you in combination, not as individual stressors. Sammy had many different stressors affecting him. He had to deal with the total effect of all stressors. If you are in a situation like Sammy, and you reach the point where you cannot deal with the accumulated effect of all the stressors, you are suffering from a condition commonly called *burnout.*

What are the Effects of Negative Stress?

The effect of negative stress (distress) can be set at three different levels. Each level has different symptoms and is more serious than the previous one.

Level one: This level is least severe. The symptoms include short periods of irritability, fatigue, worry, and frustration.

Level two: The symptoms for this level are similar to the symptoms for level one, except at level two, the symptoms will last longer, possibly as long as two weeks or more.

Level three: This level is the most serious. If you are experiencing stress at this level, you may be experiencing minor health problems, such as frequent colds, headaches, dizziness, or diarrhea.

The conditions at level three can develop into severe health problems if the effects of stress go unattended, and if you do not learn to manage or cope with your stressors. These include such problems as ulcers, high blood pressure, asthma, and diabetes.

Developing a Stress Management Program

What should you do about negative stress? You need to develop your own stress management program in order to resist the consequences of negative stress. This program should include building up your resistance to negative stress and developing techniques for avoiding negative stress, as well as developing positive coping strategies that will help you deal with the distress you cannot avoid.

Do not worry about little things

The first step in developing a stress management plan is to stop fighting things that usually cause you a lot of negative stress. You need to allow simple or minor demands on the body (minor stressors) to pass without being concerned about them or being stressed. Such minor stressors might be things that happen to you while driving a car (someone cuts in front of you), spilling a glass of milk (the responses of family members may be very stressful if you allow them to be), or meeting new people (they are probably as nervous as you are). You need to learn to respond to these minor stressors in a positive way.

If you do not respond to minor stressors in a positive manner, your irritation level will build up to a point where you will be unable to deal with the impact of a major stressor in a reasonable manner. You do not want to use up your daily energy reserve on these minor stressors.

Remaining calm in situations like this will help you remain alert and let you feel better.

Get fit

The second part of a good stress management program is to work at developing a greater energy reserve. One way this can be done is by maintaining a high level of physical fitness. This will give you greater energy and help to keep you from becoming fatigued as the demands of the day begin to wear you down. We know that everyone becomes more irritable and susceptible to minor stressors when they are tired.

You are what you eat

Proper diet is also part of your fitness and stress management program. A proper diet will help you feel good and look good. Certain aspects of your diet may increase your susceptibility to stress. Sugar

208

and caffeine are two major components of most people's diet that are high stressors. Chocolate, colas, coffee, and tea may have high concentrations of caffeine. Many prepared foods have high levels of sugar. You should attempt to limit your intake of these items. This will help keep you from being irritable, uptight, and possibly unable to cope with even minor stressors.

Develop positive coping strategies

The next step in building your stress management program should be the development of **positive coping strategies** to be used in dealing with stressors you cannot avoid. Each person must have his or her own coping techniques. As was mentioned earlier, what is a stress release for your best friend may be a stressor for you.

temporary relief may be helpful

The first approach to coping with distress is to get some temporary relief. You may do this through exercise, yoga, medicine, or just plain daydreaming. There are a number of relaxation techniques that are very helpful. You should learn at least one relaxation technique and practice it daily. Exercise is a good way to burn off adrenaline.

recognize early symptoms of stress

A second approach to developing coping techniques is to learn to recognize the early symptoms of stress. Each person reacts differently to stress. You can learn how you physically respond to stress and use those physical responses as an early warning of negative stress. If you find your jaw or facial muscles becoming tired, this might be a sign that you are reacting to stress by clenching your teeth. This physical symptom, once identified, can be used as a warning signal that you need to take a short break to relax and divert stress. Other common physical symptoms include tight neck muscles, eye strain, shoulder or back stiffness, and increased heart rate. Can you recognize any of these symptoms when something is bothering you?

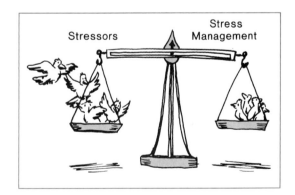

You must keep your stress scale balanced.

identify stressful situations

Another important step in developing positive coping strategies is to identify common stressful situations and define how you normally respond to those daily stressors. Once you have done this, you can modify your reaction if necessary, or concentrate on replacing your usual response with a more positive response, or coping strategy.

support groups are helpful

At times, you will be faced with stressful situations that you cannot deal with yourself. In those situations, you will need a support group, someone with whom you can talk about a particular stressor. Developing a variety of support groups, such as parents, friends at school, teachers, coaches, or counselors, can be very helpful. This will give you someone to talk to regardless of what caused you to become uptight or tense. There will be things you may not feel comfortable talking to your parents about, but you might feel free to discuss them with a peer or a physical education teacher. The more support groups you develop, the better you will feel.

You cannot cope with stress by yourself. You need support groups, such as close friends, school teachers, or family members.

Goal setting

Wise and effective goal setting, as discussed in Chapter 3, is also an important aspect of successful stress management. This is true whether you are dealing with school, work, leisure time, or your social life. Many people become frustrated and burned out from being involved in too many activities where there is little satisfaction or the expectations are unreasonable. Unreasonable expectations may mean too little is demanded (you become bored) or too much is expected (you become frustrated). You should get involved in a variety of activities that will challenge you. If you have a positive attitude and put forth a good effort, you can experience success. These types of activities are positive stressors. However, do not get involved in activities that are beyond your abilities, or in so many different activities that you do not have time to devote the effort required to be successful. Getting in "over your head," so that failure is almost a certainty, is a negative stressor.

Time management

Learning to organize your time (*time management*) is an important stress management technique. Having too many demands made on you is a common cause of negative stress. Therefore, do not get involved in too many things. Learn to say *no*. Get involved in activities which are challenging, are within your abilities, and are within the time you have. Time management may involve setting up time schedules that you follow regardless of what may come up: a specific time to do homework, a time for physical activity, and a specific time to watch television. Another technique may be keeping a priority list of things that need to be accomplished each day. The pressure of time is a major stressor for most people, and how well you manage your time will go a long way in determining how well you manage the stress in your life.

Stress Diversion Activities

Stress diversion activities are either active or passive activities which help you reduce your stress or divert stress. You should especially try to fill your leisure time with activities that are vigorous enough to provide you some of the training effects discussed earlier. These types of activities will provide you two benefits. The first benefit will be to burn up the extra adrenaline caused by stressors to prepare you for the fight or flight response. This will allow your physiological functions (heart rate, blood pressure, breathing rate) to return to normal following the exercise. The second benefit of vigorous activity is to improve your level of fitness, which will prevent you from becoming easily fatigued. If you do not become fatigued as quickly, you will be more able to cope with negative stressors. Remember, as you become fatigued, you also become more irritable and, therefore, more susceptible to negative stress.

Quiet, passive activities are also good stress diversion activities. These types of activities help you mentally forget about stressors that are bothering you. Watching television, reading a book, or listening to music may all be good stress diversion activities if they help you relax. They may also help you momentarily forget about problems and worries, and help you focus on positive things.

Remember, what is stress diversion for your friend may be a stressor for you. If you are highly competitive and concerned with winning or losing, any competitive game or activity may be a stressor. If that is the case, you need to pick a noncompetitive activity as your stress diversion activity.

Positive coping techniques can be summarized as those that work for you and may involve something in each of the following areas, to some degree:

1. high level of physical fitness

2. proper diet

3. awareness of your reaction to distress

4. awareness of common stressors

5. relaxation techniques

6. involvement in challenging activities

7. support groups

8. time management.

Negative Coping Techniques You Should Avoid

Negative responses or **negative coping techniques** are those responses you use to ease or disguise the symptoms of stress. These techniques are harmful not only to you but also to the people around you. Most of these negative techniques can be grouped into four categories: emotional, impatience, avoidance, and use of drugs and alcohol.

Being emotional will not help

A common reaction to negative stress is emotional, particularly when your feelings, ego, or self-esteem are threatened. Remember, stress causes a "fight or flight" response. Most of the time it is not appropriate for you to fight physically and you cannot run away, so the only "fight or flight" response is an emotional attempt to protect yourself or your self-esteem. A common response to criticism is to charge emotionally, "It is not my fault." This type of negative response is particularly common when the accumulated pressure of a large number

Sometimes an emotional outburst is the only response a person can make to negative stress.

of negative stressors begins to wear you down, fatigue you, or cause you to become more irritable. Many times people blurt out negative things (emotionally) they really do not believe or want to say. These negative comments may hurt the feelings of people around you or generate emotional responses from them. You should practice a number of positive coping strategies as a way of helping yourself avoid this negative technique.

Do not be impatient

Impatience is another negative response to stress. You may become impatient with yourself or with others. Impatience may occur when you have become involved in activities where your abilities are not challenged, or in activities that are far too difficult. You may also experience impatience when you have become involved in too many activities. Proper goal setting and appropriate selection of activities are important if you are going to offset the threat of impatience.

Avoidance may not be the answer

Although avoiding certain stressful situations is a positive coping technique, there are times when withdrawal or avoiding a stressor is not good. If you are afraid to talk with strangers, and avoid such stressful situations, you may not meet or get to know that boy or girl whom you really would like to meet and know. By avoiding that stressful situation, you are limiting your peer group and negatively affecting your lifestyle choices.

Avoiding certain stressful situations, like talking to someone of the opposite sex, can cause you to miss rewarding and positive experiences, thus limiting your lifestyle.

If talking in class is very stressful to you, you may choose to avoid that stressor by not volunteering or saying you do not know if the teacher calls on you. However, this may not be appropriate if your grade is partly determined by your participation in class. Avoiding this stressor is also negative, since you are not learning to handle this situation properly. It is important that you learn to deal with this problem since all people, from time to time, will find themselves in a situation where they need to talk with or in front of peers. Depending on their occupations, some people will need to do this more than others. If you choose to avoid this situation and never learn to deal with it, you will place limits on yourself in both social situations and your job. To avoid speaking in front of groups may be viewed as negative. This practice has even kept people from taking good jobs for which they were qualified. You should not let a stressor control your lifestyle choices.

Drugs and alcohol are not the answer

The fourth category of coping strategies that are considered negative is the use of drugs or alcohol. Some adults have a couple of drinks every day to relax after work. Drugs and alcohol can cause physical and mental problems, be habit forming, and may cause an individual to lose efficiency and motivation. Exercise and relaxation techniques work much better than drugs or alcohol and have a double benefit of relaxation and increasing resistance to stress. Drugs and alcohol only cover up your stress and lower your resistance to stress.

Drugs and alcohol will not eliminate stressors, but will keep you from positively coping with your problems.

Summary

Stress is the nonspecific response of the body to any demand made upon it. Stress may be either good or bad. Many factors cause stress. What may cause stress for you may not cause the same reaction in your friend.

Nearly everything you encounter is a stressor, some positive and some negative. All changes cause stress, even the pleasant ones, but major changes are the major stressors.

The body's response is the same for both positive and negative stress. Responses to stress will be both physical and mental. Many of these changes can have serious effects if left unattended.

In order to deal with stress, you need to practice positive coping strategies. Having a high level of physical fitness, eating properly, and being involved in challenging activities will help you handle your stress. Active and passive stress diversion activities may also help you cope with stressors.

The use of negative coping techniques can be dangerous. Negative methods of dealing with stress only cover up the effects of stress and do not deal with the stressor. Emotional outbursts, impatience, avoidance, or the use of drugs or alcohol are all negative coping techniques.

Study Questions

Matching

Place the letter of the correct answer in the space provided.

_____ 1. Adrenaline

_____ 2. Coping Techniques

_____ 3. Diversion

_____ 4. Fight or Flight

_____ 5. Homeostasis

_____ 6. Bad Stress

_____ 7. Physiological

_____ 8. Good Stress

A. Eustress

B. Distress

C. Things that cause stress

D. A signal to your body that a change has happened or is about to happen

E. Chemical in the body that gives you added energy

F. The mental or emotional reaction to stress

G. The biological or physical response to stress

_____ 9. Psychological

_____ 10. Stimulus

_____ 11. Stress

_____ 12. Stressors

H. The ways that you deal with stress

I. Your body's response to a demand made of it

J. The body's response to negative stress

K. Shielding from or reflecting the effects of stress

L. Internal balance or biological balance of the body

True–false

Circle "T" for all correct statements and "F" for all incorrect ones.

T   F   13. Stress is the nonspecific response of the body to any demand made upon it.

T   F   14. Stress is always present.

T   F   15. Eustress is positive stress that helps you perform.

T   F   16. Vacations can cause you stress.

T   F   17. Changes in your life will only cause stress if they affect you negatively.

T   F   18. Your body will react differently to positive and negative stress.

T   F   19. Your response to stress is only physical, not mental.

T   F   20. You are better able to handle stress if you are active.

T   F   21. Stress can cause you to become physically ill.

T   F   22. Coping strategies can be either positive or negative.

T   F   23. You should let some minor stressors pass without being concerned.

T   F   24. Avoidance should never be a part of your stress management program.

T   F   25. Sugar and caffeine may cause you to be more irritable and less able to cope with minor stress.

T   F   26. It is all right to use coping techniques that mask or hide stress.

Discussion

27. Identify and discuss the different stressors that Sammy is facing.

28. Describe the negative coping strategies Sammy could use in dealing with his stress.

29. Discuss how you could identify stressful events and how you could better cope with those events.

30. Discuss the benefits of exercise to stress diversion.

CONSUMER ISSUES 12

Chapter Objectives

As you read this chapter, look for answers to these key questions:

- What influences people to buy certain products?
- What is the most powerful tool in combating consumer fraud?
- What are five examples of unsound and worthless fitness products?
- How would you evaluate a fitness center you were considering joining?
- Why are advertisements claiming fast weight reduction and spot reduction fraudulent weight-reducing schemes?
- What are anabolic steroids and why should you avoid them?
- How can teenagers combat false advertising claims?

When you have completed this chapter, you should understand the meaning of these vocabulary terms:

consumer
diuretics
anabolic steroids

You as a Consumer

You can't always judge a book by the cover.

What do you have in common with neighbors, grandparents, entertainers, and professional athletes? All of you are consumers. A **consumer** is a person who buys goods and services. You have many choices as a consumer. You choose what to buy, where to buy, and when to buy. You also have to decide how to get the best value for your money. You will become a satisfied consumer by making wise purchasing decisions.

Many companies cater only to the teen market.

Each year teenagers spend billions of dollars on clothing, records, tapes, magazines, athletic gear, and many other items. In fact, teen spending power is so large that many companies cater only to the teen market. After studying this chapter, you will be better prepared to make wise decisions about spending your money on items, brand names, and services related to physical fitness and sports.

What Influences Your Buying Decisions?

What influenced your buying decision when you bought your last pair of jeans? Did you buy the same brand name of jeans you bought before? Did you buy the brand advertised in the latest issue of a teen magazine? Or, was your decision influenced by the brand your friends wear?

Influence of peers

Many teens are influenced by their friends to buy certain items or brand names. You enjoy the feeling of belonging to a group and naturally like to be similar or conform to what your friends are doing. While it is fun and natural to follow the crowd, it is important to be sure you are buying what is best for you. Ask yourself the following questions:

Am I buying a fad item that is popular today but will soon be out of fashion?
Am I getting the best value for my money?
Am I spending twice as much money for a name brand item?

Friends often have a great influence on what you buy.

Influence of habit

Buying decisions are frequently influenced by buying habits. You may think that other brands are inferior if you have a habit of always buying name brand items. You may be missing excellent bargains if you always shop at one store. Try to fight off any tendency to be a consumer snob.

Influence of advertising

Advertising can have a powerful influence on your buying decisions. Advertising is found in all types of media that surround you every day. Whatever the form, advertising offers many advantages and lets consumers know what products or services are available. It lets people know about sales, and it introduces new products, along with the benefits of those products. There are also disadvantages to advertising. Sometimes it encourages people to buy things they do not need. It can also be misleading. For example, some ads make exaggerated claims in regard to your fitness, exercise, and sports needs.

Some experts believe that television commercials damage young people's self-esteem by portraying people in almost supernatural ways. Do not allow such commercials to convince you that you are not attractive, witty, or physically capable when compared to people seen on television. This is exactly what the advertisers want to happen, because the products in the commercials then appear as the solution for people not feeling good enough about themselves.

You say I'll get bigger muscles in three days? Sure, I want one!

Many people waste money on useless products.

Have You Been Ripped Off?

Do you like to get ripped off? The obvious answer to this question is NO! While this is true, many people appear ready to buy any product which has some promise of helping them look and feel better. Billions of dollars are spent every year by Americans on questionable products. All of us have been victimized by false advertisements at some time or another, but teenagers are an extremely susceptible group because they have little information and may not have separated fact from fiction.

Teenagers have a strong desire to look as good as possible. Because of this, many companies will advertise almost anything that puts forth the promise of helping teenagers look more attractive. Teenagers are targets of advertising and, as a result, spend a lot of money on glamour products. However, they are often hindered in their buying decisions by a lack of knowledge.

Knowledge is the key

Knowledge is probably the only way of combating false advertising. It does not take much knowledge to be able to spot unethical or worthless claims. You must beware when it comes to any treatment, device, or product being promoted to make your body more attractive and beautiful. You need to be especially leery of products or treatments promising amazing results in a very short time. Your body cannot be reshaped overnight.

It is easy to say "No" to false advertising claims if you have knowledge.

Are you a knowledgeable consumer?

Physical fitness consumers must be knowledgeable in order to get the greatest benefit from their money. Knowledge is the key to power, consumer power, your power! You must be able to determine which advertisements are sound and which are unsound. Remember, people selling unsound products do not want you to be knowledgeable about the real effects of their products. They would much rather have you believe everything you see, hear, or read about the thousands of products on the market. The end result is that they make money, and the uninformed consumer finds very little satisfaction from the products because few of the promised results actually take place.

Spot Reduction: The Biggest Myth

Many people want to lose pounds in one certain area of the body, such as the stomach or thighs. You may have friends who would like to lose a few pounds in a specific area. In order to lose these unwanted pounds, people want to believe advertisements which promise fast and easy results if they just purchase a certain product.

The misconception that fat can be reduced or removed from specific areas of the body is probably the most obvious abuse of established knowledge about the way the body responds to exercise. It has been shown many times through research that spot reduction is impossible. Many people still hold to the idea that exercising an isolated part of the body, where the fat has accumulated, trims fat from that specific area. This is simply not true. There is no known means by which fat may be broken down and lost from one part of your body. If this were true, many overweight people would do what was necessary to trim unsightly fat from their stomachs, hips, or thighs.

Many exercise gadgets, devices, and programs are based on the misconception that if muscle groups beneath the fat are used, the fat will

NEW REDUCING PAJAMAS

Reduce Waist, Hips, Thighs, Etc. While You Sleep!

No drugs!
No stimulants!
No hunger!

go away. The most prevalent example of this is that sit-ups will reduce fat on the stomach. Ask ten of your friends how they would reduce the fat on their stomachs and, in all probability, nine out of ten will answer by saying "sit-ups." Stretching exercises are frequently used to get rid of fat in a specific spot. Some of these exercises serve a very useful purpose, but that purpose is not the reduction of fat from a specific part of the body.

False Advertising Claims

"Just lie back, relax. You can lose as much weight as you want and never gain any of it back."

Would you not agree this advertisement is very impressive from the standpoint of sounding easy to do? Imagine, all you have to do is lie down and relax. The rest of the advertisement, a full-page ad which is not included here, used such phrases as, "will unleash unused powers of your subconscious mind," "ignite natural fat burners," "launch an attack on stubborn bulges," "break down the fat on thighs, stomach, and fannys," "shrink the size of your stomach," and finally "get rid of your hunger." Typically, the reader's attention is immediately drawn to the glamorous woman also shown in the ad. The final bait thrown out to tempt the buyer is "if you just send in $19.95 plus $2.00 shipping charge plus tax, you will receive a cassette tape which will guarantee beautiful results, and you can be just as attractive as the young woman in the ad."

Exercise Gadgets and Gimmicks

A complete list of useless fat-reduction exercise gadgets and products would be extremely long. The following are examples of unsound exercise gadgets and gimmicks.

A. **Massage** does not break up fat and allow it to be burned off. Massage feels good and may help loosen up tight muscles, but it does not cause weight loss.

This machine can not help you lose weight.

Wearing a plastic suit can be hazardous to your health.

B. **Vibrating belts** and other devices that vibrate or shake to massage a part of your body do not break up fat, help you lose weight, or help improve your physical fitness level.

C. **Sauna baths** have become popular and they may feel great, but they have no effect on weight loss.

D. **Motorized exercise bikes,** or any other motorized exercise devices that do all the work, will not cause you to lose weight or help improve your physical fitness level.

E. **Plastic or rubberized sweat and sauna suits** make people sweat a lot, but they prevent the evaporation of heat from the body and hinder the ability of the body to cool itself. The weight loss which occurs when wearing these items is water loss, not fat loss. After you sweat off a few pounds of body fluids during a vigorous workout, you will regain the weight as soon as you drink fluids.

F. **Body wraps** have been popular through the years. People selling such products claim that you can lose inches of fat rapidly by wearing body wraps. Some body wraps are soaked in a solution that is supposed to have some magic capabilities. There is absolutely no truth to the statement that people can lose weight or increase their physical fitness level by wearing body wraps.

H. **Electric stimulators** cause a mild electric current to go to the muscle and make it move. Such devices do very little for weight loss or physical fitness, and they could be dangerous to some people.

I. **Bust developers** have been a popular form of mis-advertisement for over a century. It is not surprising that such devices are still popular, since many females believe they need to have bigger breasts in order to look more like the adult females seen in magazines and on television. Certain weight training exercises for the chest may enhance breast appearance by firming up or toning the muscles underneath the breast, but nothing can be done to increase the size of the breasts.

Drugs and Weight Control

Appetite suppressants and thyroid hormones are two general categories of drugs commonly used in the treatment of overweight and obese people. These drugs supposedly increase the body's metabolic rate and therefore cause the body to burn more calories. Research has shown that only a small percentage of overweight and obese people have a hormone problem. Most have simply developed extremely poor exercise and nutritional habits.

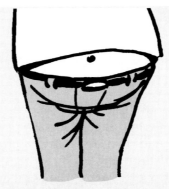

FLAB AWAY
No appetite control capsule works harder to help you lose weight.
New! European discovery by Dr. Adipose

What about diuretics?

Diuretics are used to control different types of edema (accumulation of fluid in body tissues), congestive heart failure, and high blood pressure. They are occasionally prescribed for women with high blood pressure who experience weight gain due to water retention before their menstrual period. Diuretics do not promote real weight loss. Any weight loss starts coming right back with your first glass of water. Diuretics may be dangerous for the following reasons. They may:

A. lead to a dangerously low potassium level, which can cause heart problems.

B. upset the body's chemical balance.

C. increase cardiovascular problems for people with high blood pressure.

D. cause blood clotting problems during menstruation.

E. damage the kidneys if used continually.

Diuretics are a very poor solution to a weight gain dilemma. Again, water loss is not true weight reduction because no calories are burned. Those who use diuretics are only fooling themselves! Do not be an uninformed consumer.

Fad diets

Many Americans seem only too willing to pay any price for a quick, simple, and comfortable method of getting rid of their excess body fat. At first glance, it might appear that a number of programs and products on the market will accomplish this, but the fact is that a simple, easy cure for being overweight or obese remains to be discovered. While some diets or remedies may bring about temporary weight reduction, most are not only ineffective but are also hazardous to your health. You should be very skeptical of crash diets recommended in popular diet books, appetite suppressant drugs, and any *miracle food* that comes with money-back guarantees.

Anabolic Steroids

Athletes are vulnerable to claims that certain substances can enhance performance. You have probably heard of the abuse of anabolic steroids by body builders, professional football players, and track athletes. Many other people experiment with these substances in an effort to improve their physical appearance and to become stronger. Research studies indicate that teenagers (almost entirely males) are also using steroids more frequently. It is extremely important that teenagers understand the very serious side effects of the use of anabolic steroids.

What are anabolic steroids?

Anabolic steroids are a synthetic version of testosterone, the male sex hormone. Synthetic anabolic steroids are complex chemicals that the body does not handle easily or naturally. Synthetic anabolic steroids are related to testosterone in structure and function, but the chemical structures have been modified in ways that alter their effects on the body.

The male testes produce testosterone naturally. At puberty, males may have as much as a 20-fold increase in testosterone naturally. Testosterone stimulates the development of bone, muscle, and hair growth, as well as affecting a person's emotional development.

Effects on the body

The body shuts down its own production of testosterone if these synthetic substances are administered orally or by injection. The body reacts this way because it recognizes there is more than an adequate supply of testosterone in it. The testicles will shrink if anabolic steriods are taken for a long period of time, since the testosterone-producing cells in the body are no longer active.

Say NO to steroids.

It must be recognized that these drugs are extremely dangerous to anyone taking them. The following are some of the many undesirable side effects associated with steroid use:

A. liver and kidney damage
B. decrease in ultimate height
C. increased risk of cancer
D. scalp hair loss
E. appearance of acne
F. decrease in size of the testicles and impotency
G. increased aggression and unpredictable mood changes
H. reduction of breast size in women

Young people have more problems with anabolic steroids than older people. One difference has to do with bone growth. These drugs can cause premature closure of the growth plates on the ends of the long bones in your body. This can have a very serious effect on your growth. It can decrease the height to which you would normally grow.

The more a person uses steroids, the greater the risk of developing one of the many conditions identified as harmful side effects. Realizing what is known about steroids, you would be wise to adhere to the position stated by the American College of Sports Medicine. This group recommends that, because enhanced performance cannot be documented while dangerous side effects can, everyone should refrain from steroid use. Once again, the answer to self-improvement is not found in a pill or a bottle.

Are Health Clubs Worth the Money?

The number of fitness centers has expanded rapidly in recent years, since more and more people have become fitness and appearance conscious. Your decision whether or not to join a fitness center may depend on such factors as cost and your personal needs.

Most fitness centers will conduct an orientation session to the use of the exercise equipment and make an effort to develop a personal fitness program to meet your individual needs. In most cases, these orientation sessions will be conducted by knowledgeable people. Occasionally, however, instructors will have a very weak background in how to exercise properly. For your own protection and for your own best development, have your mind sensitized for certain myths about exercise, such as spot reduction. If you detect instructors with a lack of knowledge, take their instruction with a "grain of salt" and look for another fitness center.

Use objective criteria to evaluate a fitness center. Do not let the glitter or a high-pressure salesperson influence you.

By learning all you can about your body and which exercises are best for what purposes, you will not need anyone else telling you what you need to do. You may not even need to join a health club or fitness center. Do some comparative shopping if you decide to join a fitness center. These centers frequently have specials, and you can save considerable amounts of money. It is also a common practice to try to get you to sign up for a multi-year agreement, with the bait being that your average yearly amount of money for joining will be less than if you just join for one year. It is strongly advised that you avoid this type of agreement. Although it sounds like a good deal at the time, many people stop using the health club after a while and thus end up spending a large amount of money for the short-term use of the health club.

Additional Advice on Products

Beware of testimonials!

The following are a few more tips to help you recognize unsound advertisements.

A. Beware of testimonials! Have you ever wondered why many people offer testimonials for various products? You have the hang of it now, if your answer is money. The people who make the testimonials are paid by the company to make their statements. Are there good testimonials? Yes, but you must read and listen carefully to what they say. You should also be aware of any of your friends who start talking about products which have helped them to lose their fat in just three days or some similar claim.

B. The offer generally involves a special gift for fast action. If it sounds too good to be true, it probably is.

C. The location of the ad may be another tip-off. It is usually placed in the back of the magazine or in some other out-of-the-way place.

D. Is it likely that one product can do everything? No! One product cannot do everything although it is easy to find advertisements which make this claim.

In a free-enterprise system such as we have in this country, people are allowed and certainly encouraged to start small businesses to provide services to others, if there is a need. They obviously need to advertise to promote the sale of their services in whatever form they may take. People frequently get greedy for more quick money and make all sorts of exaggerated claims about their products.

The Federal Trade Commission and the Food and Drug Administration are unable to effectively regulate the sale of fraudulent weight-reducing schemes since companies are not required to provide evidence of their beneficial claims prior to public sale of their products.

What Can You Do To Combat False Advertising Claims?

Be a responsible consumer. Take action when you have been exposed to a false claim.

You may wonder how you can do anything to stop false advertising if government agencies are slow and at times ineffective. There are things which you can do as an individual or as a group (teens) to combat false advertising. First, it is good to remember that many people who are trying to make a living from the sale of useless products assume that teenagers are not smart enough to filter through the big words and fancy promises and recognize that certain products are worthless. Are they in for a surprise!

Take this one step further and tell your friends about the advertisements. You can become an advocate for teenage consumerism. Write letters to the editors of the various magazines, criticizing products they are advertising. A final suggestion is to call your local Better Business Bureau and explain why you believe the advertising for a particular product is fraudulent.

Everyone wants to look and feel as good as possible. There are no easy methods to accomplish these goals. No pills, diets, or secret formulas will do the trick.

Be a smart shopper! Control your money carefully, and remember that the knowledge you have gained is power in your pocket. Use it wisely.

Summary

Hundreds of unsound products are sold every year to consumers who want to be more physically attractive. People selling these products are experts at making you believe you can improve yourself, usually in a very short period of time. They are successful in selling worthless products because many consumers do not have the necessary knowledge to recognize untrue statements. You can protect yourself, your family, and your friends from being ripped off, just by understanding some basic information related to how the body reacts to exercise and proper health practices. You can become a strong and effective advocate for sound advertising and play a very important role in getting worthless products off the shelves at your local stores.

Study Questions

True–false

Circle the "T" for all correct statements and the "F" for all incorrect ones.

T F   1. Companies often target teenagers to sell personal improvement products.

T F   2. People selling useless products want the consumers to be knowledgeable about products which have to do with looking and feeling good.

T F   3. You can reduce or remove fat from specific areas of your body by exercising that area.

T F   4. Doing "sit-ups" will remove fat from a person's stomach.

T F   5. Massage helps a person to become physically fit.

T F   6. Motorized exercise devices that do all of the work will not cause you to lose weight or help you to improve your fitness level.

T F   7. Wearing a rubberized sweat suit in hot weather can be very dangerous.

T F   8. Research has shown that a large percentage of overweight people have hormone problems.

T F   9. Diuretics may upset the body's chemical balance.

T F   10. Fluid loss through the use of diuretics is a permanent weight loss.

T F   11. A good way to tell whether a product is sound is to read the personal testimonials.

T F   12. Teenagers can help get unsound products off the market.

T   F   13. Knowledge can help you save money and keep you from buying worthless products.

T   F   14. The general use of anabolic steroids is considered drug abuse.

T   F   15. The use of anabolic steroids can cause a decrease in the normal height to which you would grow.

Discussion

16. Identify something that you purchased recently. What influenced you to buy the item? What influenced you to buy from that specific store? Was a brand name involved and, if so, what influenced you to buy that brand name?

17. A friend is concerned about his fat stomach and tells you he is doing sit-ups to get rid of the fat. You immediately know he is on the wrong track. What would you tell him? Of what value are sit-ups?

18. Your mother is concerned about her legs because they are getting flabby. She asks you if flexibility exercises could do her any good. What is your answer? What type of exercise would be important for her to do? What other factor might be of extreme importance?

19. Your girlfriend wants to join a health club and she does not know which one to join. What can you advise her?

20. It would appear that those persons who direct companies which produce ``questionable'' products believe teenagers are not the brightest consumers. What can teens do to counter this belief?

Chapter Objectives

As you read this chapter, look for answers to these key questions:

- What are considered the best activities for you to improve physical fitness?
- What are some of the most popular exercise programs?
- Why is it important for you to develop skills in lifetime sports?
- Why should you consider health needs before selecting activities for your personal fitness program?
- Why are benefits from stress diversion activities considered very personal?
- How do your personality and attitudes affect your selection of exercise programs and sports activities?
- How does the environment, availability of facilities, and the cost of the activity enter into selecting activities for your personal fitness program?

When you have completed this chapter, you should understand the meaning of these vocabulary terms:

planned program	circuit training
high-impact aerobics	interval training
low-impact aerobics	sports skills activities
calisthenics	lifetime sports

Which Activities Are Best?

Quality is never an accident; it is always the result of effort.

In order to be fit and healthy, as well as look good and feel good for a lifetime, you will need to engage in some kind of regular exercise program. The key to developing a successful personal fitness program is to design a program that is right for you. The selection of activities depends on many factors.

- What components of physical fitness do you need to improve most?
- What kinds of exercises and activities do you enjoy?
- What sports skills do you have or need?
- What kind of activities help you manage your stress?
- Will you be exercising alone or with others?
- Where will you be exercising?
- Will you need special equipment or facilities?

No single physical activity is best for everyone. You have to select activities that best meet your needs. Try to include a variety of activities in your personal fitness program to avoid boredom and to keep exercise fun and interesting. Do not be afraid to try a new or different activity; however, do not hesitate to stop an activity if you do not enjoy it. It is important that you do not become a physical fitness dropout just because you picked the wrong activity. Keep trying until you find activities you really enjoy. You will continue to participate in an activity you enjoy.

Categories of Activities

In order to determine the activities that are best for you, you will need to become acquainted with and evaluate the many exercise programs which are now available. Exercise and activities can be divided into two groups: (1) exercise programs and (2) sports activities.

Exercise programs

Exercise programs can be pre-determined by someone else or designed by you. It is important to remember that any exercise program should be based on the principles of training discussed in earlier chapters to assure both benefit and safety.

Exercise programs seen on television and on video tapes are examples of planned programs.

Pre-determined programs usually include specific exercises for persons of specific fitness levels or ages. These are sometimes referred to as "set" or **planned programs.** Aerobic dance classes, exercise programs seen on television and on video tapes, circuit training, and fitness trails found in many recreation parks are examples of such programs. These activities can help you get started in an exercise program. They are easy to follow and require little planning on your part. However, do not feel that you must complete the entire workout the first time through. It is important to pick and choose which ones best suit you and meet your needs.

Your overall personal fitness program should include several different exercise programs in order to meet all your needs. You are encouraged to try different exercise programs. Some sample planned programs are provided to assist you in developing your own program. The following are some of the more popular exercise programs.

aerobic dance

Aerobic dance is a popular exercise program for people of all ages. Aerobic dance routines include a combination of dance steps and calisthenics done to upbeat, popular music. Aerobic dance can be high-impact or low-impact. **High-impact aerobics** include jumping, bouncing, and running. **Low-impact aerobics** include vigorous arm movements while keeping one foot in contact with the ground at all times. You can develop your own aerobic dance routines, participate in programs at health clubs and recreation departments, or follow those seen on television and on video tapes.

Aerobic dance is a popular exercise program for people of all ages.

aqua dynamics

Aqua dynamics is an exercise program done in the water. You do not have to be a swimmer to participate in this kind of exercise program. Many exercises in aqua dynamics are similar to calisthenics. Because of the buoyancy provided by the water, aqua dynamics is a very popular exercise program among people who have been injured and handicapped persons.

Aqua dynamics is a very popular exercise program among handicapped individuals.

bicycling

Bicycling is one of the most popular exercise programs for developing cardiovascular fitness and muscular endurance in the legs. Bicycling must be done continuously for at least 20 minutes in order to have an aerobic effect. You should try to maintain steady, continuous pedaling rather than coasting.

Sample Bicycling Program

Week	Frequency/Wk	Distance	Time
1	3	2.0 miles	12:00
2	3	2.0 miles	10:00
3	3	2.5 miles	13:00
4	3	3.0 miles	20:00
5	4	3.0 miles	20:00

calisthenics

Calisthenics are exercises that use your own body parts or body weight as resistance. Such exercises are convenient to do because they require little or no equipment and can be done very easily at home. Calisthenics are used for warm-up, flexibility, and development of muscular strength and muscular endurance. Running-in-place, side-leg raises, push-ups, sit-ups, and pull-ups are examples of calisthenics.

circuit training

Circuit training is an exercise program in which you make one or more trips around a prescribed course, stopping at each station along the way to perform a specified exercise. This type of exercise program stresses continuous activity. The intensity of a circuit can be made more difficult by increasing the repetitions of the exercise at each station, by decreasing the time required to complete the circuit, or by a combination of both.

1. Bench Step
2. Upright Rowing
3. Doorway Leg Press
4. Front Curl
5. Sit-Ups
6. Sprinter
7. Pull-Ups
8. Heel Raiser
9. Isometric—Head Push
10. Standing Press
11. Rope Jumping
12. Bar Dips

fitness trails

Today fitness trails are located in many recreation parks and on school grounds. A fitness trail is an established route of considerable distance with numerous exercise stations dispersed along the way. Signs that describe and illustrate each exercise and indicate the number of repetitions are located at each station. You can walk or jog between stations, stop and perform the exercise at each station, and continue on until you have completed the trail.

interval training

Interval training is an exercise program that involves a series of exercises interspersed with rest periods. Interval training is usually associated with endurance training in running and swimming, but the general principles are applicable to any kind of exercise program. There are four variables involved in interval training: (1) speed or rate, (2) distance or length of time, (3) rest interval, and (4) number of repetitions. One or all of the variables can be altered to change the intensity of the workout.

An Example of Interval Training Applied to Various Activities

Activity	Freq./Wk	Distance	Time	Rest	Repetitions
Jogging	3	220 yds.	0:45	2:00	5
Swimming	3	50 yds.	2:00	1:00	6
Bicycling	3	.5 miles	2:00	1:00	8

jogging

Jogging is one of the most popular forms of aerobic exercise. Many people believe jogging is the best overall exercise for developing and maintaining cardiovascular fitness. Like walking, almost everyone can jog. You can jog almost anywhere and almost any time. You can jog alone, with someone, or with a group of people. The only special equipment required is a good pair of running shoes.

Sample Jogging Program

Week	Frequency/Wk	Distance	Time
1	3	1.0 mile	12:00
2	3	1.5 miles	18:00
3	3	1.5 miles	16:00
4	3	2.0 miles	26:00
5	4	2.0 miles	24:00

rope jumping

Rope jumping is an excellent cardiovascular fitness activity that only requires a few simple skills and a rope. Many people jump rope when there is no opportunity to jog, swim, or bicycle, such as in a motel room when traveling. In designing a rope jumping program, you should use a continuous, progressive routine. You should progress very slowly in order to prevent injuries. The length of a rope should be such that it will reach your armpits when held to the ground beneath your feet.

swimming

Swimming is an excellent exercise program for developing and maintaining physical fitness. Virtually every muscle is utilized as you propel yourself through the water. Swimming for physical fitness is done in laps at a mild or moderate pace. One advantage that swimming has over other exercise programs is that it is less conducive to injuries.

Rope jumping provides a safe means of developing cardiovascular fitness when you are traveling.

Sample Swimming Program

Week	Frequency/Wk	Distance	Time
1	3	300 yds.	12:30
2	3	300 yds.	10:30
3	3	350 yds.	12:00
4	3	350 yds.	12:00
5	4	400 yds.	15:00

If you do not know how to swim, contact your local parks and recreation department, YMCA, or college. These organizations usually offer swimming classes for all ages. You may be surprised at how easy it is to learn to swim.

walking

Walking is a very popular form of aerobic exercise. The biggest advantage of walking is that it can be done easily, without wear and tear on the body. Almost everyone can do it. You can walk almost anywhere and almost any time. A sturdy, comfortable pair of shoes is the only equipment necessary. When you are walking for physical fitness, you should not stroll in a leisurely manner. Instead, you should walk at a steady pace that is brisk enough to make your heart beat faster and cause you to breathe more deeply and rapidly.

Sample Walking Program

Week	Frequency/Wk	Distance	Time
1	3	1.0 mile	15:00
2	3	1.5 miles	22:30
3	3	2.0 miles	30:00
4	3	2.0 miles	26:40
5	4	2.0 miles	26:40

weight training

Weight training is considered to be the quickest and most effective way to develop muscular strength and muscular endurance. It is a very popular exercise program among men and is gaining popularity among women as the myths about femininity and muscle-boundness are discredited. Weight training can be in the form of free weights or machines.

Different exercise programs have different benefits. You must select the programs that are best for you. The contributions of various exercise programs to the health-related components of physical fitness and stress diversion are illustrated in the Exercise Programs Analysis Chart.

Exercise Programs Analysis Chart

Exercise Programs	Flexibility	Cardio-vascular Fitness	Muscular Strength	Muscular Endur-ance	Body Com-position	Stress Diversion	Overall Benefit (Total Points)	Overall Average
Aerobic Dance	3	3	1	2	3	3	15	2.5
Aqua Dynamics	2	2	2	2	2	3	13	2.2
Bicycling	1	3	2	2	3	3	14	2.3
Calisthenics	3	1	2	2	1	3	12	2.0
Circuit Training	2	2	2	3	2	3	14	2.3
Fitness Trails	2	2	2	3	2	3	14	2.3
Interval Training	1	3	2	2	3	3	14	2.3
Jogging	1	3	1	2	3	3	13	2.2
Rope Jumping	1	3	1	2	2	3	12	2.0
Swimming	2	3	2	2	3	3	15	2.5
Walking	1	2	1	2	3	3	12	2.0
Weight Training	2	1	3	3	1	3	13	2.2

Rating Scale: 3—High   2—Medium   1—Low

Sports activities may supplement more traditional physical fitness activities.

Sports activities

Sports skills activities are those activities which help you develop sports skills and satisfy your need for competition. Some people prefer to get their exercise through participation in sports activities. Some individuals are more easily motivated by sports activities than by other forms of exercise. Keep in mind that even top athletes supplement their sports training with flexibility, cardiovascular, muscular strength, and muscular endurance programs. Whatever sports activities you choose, you will enjoy them more if you have an adequate level of physical fitness.

Your high school years are generally oriented to team or group activities, but as you get older you may lose interest in these activities. You may also experience more difficulty finding opportunities to participate in team activities as you get older. That is why it is important to develop skills in individual sports. Individual sports are sometimes called **lifetime sports,** since they can be engaged in for a lifetime. Golf, racquetball, and tennis are examples of such activities. You should develop skills in as many lifetime sports as practical while in high school. You will develop these new skills more quickly now than as an adult. Also, the more sports skills you possess, the less limited you will be in your lifestyle choices, now and as an adult.

It is important to develop skills in lifetime sports.

Before choosing sports activities to be included in your personal fitness program, you should understand the benefits gained from each activity. Benefits from participation in sports activities will vary according to the activity and the skill you possess. Some activities can be very beneficial in meeting your health-related fitness needs if you possess the skill level required to obtain a sufficient workout. Generally, the more skill you possess, the greater the benefit will be. Some activities, such as bowling and softball, contribute very little to the development of fitness. Others, such as soccer and basketball, are much more conducive to developing physical fitness.

The contributions of various sports activities to the health-related components of physical fitness and stress diversion are illustrated in the Sports Activities Analysis Chart. The contributions to health-related physical fitness are based upon an individual possessing a reasonable level of skill in the activities. The contributions to stress diversion are based on how a majority of people would respond.

Sports Activities Analysis Chart

Sports Activities	Flexibility	Cardio-vascular Fitness	Muscular Strength	Muscular Endur-ance	Body Com-position	Stress Diversion	Overall Benefit (Total Points)	Overall Average
Archery	1	1	2	2	1	2	9	1.5
Backpacking/Hiking	2	2	2	3	2	3	14	2.3
Badminton	2	3	1	1	2	1	10	1.7
Basketball	1	3	1	2	3	1	11	1.8
Billiards/Pool	1	1	1	1	1	2	7	1.2
Bowling	1	1	1	1	1	2	7	1.2
Canoeing	1	2	1	2	2	3	11	1.8
Dance (Social)	1	1	1	1	1	3	8	1.3
Diving	3	1	1	1	1	2	9	1.5
Fencing	2	2	1	2	1	1	9	1.5
Football (Flag/Touch)	1	2	1	2	1	1	8	1.3
Golf (Walking)	2	1	1	2	1	1	8	1.3
Gymnastics	3	1	3	3	1	2	13	2.2
Handball/Paddleball/Racquetball	2	3	1	2	3	1	12	2.0
Hockey (Field)	2	2	1	2	1	1	9	1.5
Horseback Riding	1	1	1	1	1	3	8	1.3
Judo/Karate	3	1	2	2	1	3	12	2.0
Lacrosse	2	2	1	2	1	1	9	1.5
Rugby	2	3	1	2	1	1	10	1.7
Sailing	2	1	1	1	1	3	9	1.5
Scuba Diving	1	1	1	2	1	3	9	1.5
Skating (Ice/Roller)	1	2	1	2	2	3	11	1.8
Skiing (Cross Country)	1	3	2	2	3	3	14	2.3
Skiing (Downhill)	1	2	2	2	1	3	11	1.8
Soccer	2	3	1	2	3	1	12	2.0
Softball	1	1	1	1	1	2	7	1.2
Speedball	2	2	1	2	1	1	9	1.5
Surfing	2	1	1	2	1	3	10	1.7
Table Tennis	1	1	1	1	1	2	7	1.2
Tennis	2	2	1	1	2	1	9	1.5
Volleyball	2	1	1	1	1	2	8	1.3
Waterpolo	3	3	1	3	2	1	13	2.2

Considerations Before Selecting Activities

Several factors will affect your decisions about which activities will be most beneficial for your personal fitness program. These factors include:

- health needs
- sports skills
- stress diversion
- personality and attitudes
- financial considerations
- availability of facilities
- environmental considerations

Health needs

How physically fit are you? What health-related components of physical fitness do you need to improve the most? In order for your personal fitness program to be successful, you must determine your needs by assessing the health-related components of fitness. The components you are the weakest in should be given the most attention. If, for example, you need to improve your cardiovascular fitness, you should participate in activities which will elevate your pulse rate and maintain it for at least 15 to 30 minutes. Activities such as jogging, bicycling, and swimming or sports such as basketball and soccer would be appropriate selections to improve cardiovascular fitness.

You should also consider any health problems or physical impairments you may have before selecting the types of activities that will be included in your personal fitness program. Swimming, jogging, and riding your bike are all excellent ways of improving cardiovascular fitness,

Physical disabilities

but they all demand something different from you. An individual who is overweight may not want to begin jogging because of the strain it would place on the legs and feet. For an overweight individual, walking, swimming, or bicycling may be better choices to improve cardiovascular fitness.

Other health needs which may be considered in the selection of activities are:

- If you are trying to gain or lose weight, consider the caloric cost of activities.
- As you grow older, your interest in sports will change, accessibility of other people to participate in team sports will be less, and the amount of time available to exercise may decrease.
- If you have a physical disability, this may limit activities in which you are able to participate.
- A health problem may limit the degree in which you engage in vigorous activity. You should select specific activities that will help to improve your problem. For example, do exercises that will strengthen the lower back to prevent low-back pain.

Sports skills

Your skill level will influence your success and continued participation in sports activities. Some activities require a great deal of skill. You should study the different sports activities to determine which ones are best for you, based on the level of skill you possess. Remember, an activity good for someone else may not be good for you. Try various sports activities and evaluate them to determine if they are beneficial for you. Determine the skill requirements of the activity, such as agility, balance, power, reaction time, coordination, and speed. For example, if you are very agile and the sport selected requires a high degree of agility, you will be successful. If you experience success, you are more likely to continue the activity and, therefore, improve your physical fitness.

Stress diversion

Stress diversion activities include those activities that would help you manage your stress. Activities that serve as stress diversion may also meet health or sport skills needs. Benefits from stress diversion activities are very personal. What may be a good stress diversion activity for you may not be good for your friends. Activities that are highly competitive are usually considered poor stress diversion activities. However, if you can participate in a competitive activity, such as tennis, and not be caught up in winning and losing, it could be beneficial to you in controlling your stress.

In the Sports Activities Analysis Chart, the stress diversion evaluations are based on how a majority of people would respond. The chart is meant only as a guide, since stress diversion is a personal matter. In evaluating activities for stress diversion, you must consider how *you* would respond.

Coping with stress

Personality and attitudes

Your personality and attitudes are important factors that should be considered in the selection of activities for your personal fitness program. Do you like exercising alone or with others? Do you like to compete with others or only against yourself? Do you prefer activities that are self-directed or coached? Do you prefer to exercise indoors or outdoors?

Your personality and attitudes have a bearing on the activities you select.

alone or with others

Some people prefer to be alone with their thoughts during physical activity, while some like to exercise with others. Some individuals are more successful in exercising regularly if they have someone else with whom to exercise. A partner, a group of friends, or family members can provide encouragement. Exercising with others may also help develop or reaffirm friendships. However, do not assume that you have to follow your friend's program. Remember, your exercise program must be individualized to meet your needs, or you will not be satisfied.

competitive or non-competitive

Some individuals are highly competitive and prefer activities in which they compete against other people. If this describes you, be careful not to let your exercise program become a contest. Remember, you should exercise at your own level. Some people, on the other hand, do not like competing against others. They prefer to work on their personal fitness program alone by competing against themselves.

self-directed or coached

Some people prefer self-directed activities. These are activities they conduct themselves, such as walking, jogging, or bicycling. Such individuals usually possess internal motivation and enjoy competing against themselves. However, some individuals prefer activities, such as aerobic dance, that are conducted or coached by someone else. Such individuals tend to get "psyched" by their coaches or instructors.

indoors or outdoors

Exercising outdoors offers variety in scenery and weather. The beauty of the outdoors motivates many people to participate in various activities such as hiking, skiing, sailing, and canoeing. Exercising indoors offers shelter from the weather and can offer the convenience of exercising at home. Some activities, such as rope jumping, can be done indoors or outdoors. Because some activities can be affected by weather, you may want to consider choosing an alternate activity. Then you can change activities, if need be, and still stay on your regular exercise schedule.

Financial considerations

Much of what you need to exercise is free. Many activities require little or no equipment. For example, you can walk, jog, and do many exercises with virtually no cost. Also, keep in mind that many communities offer free or inexpensive recreation facilities and physical activity classes. What you will need to purchase will be determined by the kind of activities you include in your personal fitness program. Sometimes the cost of an activity may be prohibitive, thus eliminating it from consideration.

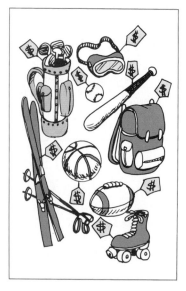

Cost will have a bearing on the activities you select.

Availability of facilities

The availability of facilities should also be considered before selecting activities you will include in your personal fitness program. Swimming is an excellent activity, but if a pool is not available, you need to consider something else. The same thing is true about the other components of your fitness program. What facilities or equipment do you have access to that can develop muscular strength and endurance? You may need to rely on push-ups, sit-ups, and pull-ups, or on free weights if weight machines are not available.

Environmental considerations

Often the environment is a major factor in determining what type of activity in which to participate. Extremes in weather, either very hot and humid or very cold, could influence you in the type of activity you plan and the time of day you exercise. In highly populated areas, air pollution and personal safety are also factors that must be taken into consideration.

Summary

The number of exercise programs and sports activities to choose from are virtually endless. You must remember that any exercise program should be based on the principles of training to assure both benefit and safety. The best activities are those that you not only enjoy, but also meet your individual needs.

Before choosing exercise programs and sports activities for your personal fitness program, you should understand the benefits gained from each activity. Benefits will vary according to the activity and the skill you possess.

In order for your personal fitness program to be successful, you must determine your physical fitness needs. Once you identify your fitness needs, specific activities can be selected for the various health-related components needing improvement. Health problems, sports skills, stress diversion, personality and attitudes, cost, availability of facilities, and environment are also factors which will affect your selection of activities. Remember, the key to developing a successful personal fitness program is designing a program that is right for you.

Study Questions

True—false

Circle "T" for all correct statements and "F" for all incorrect ones.

T   F   1. No single activity or exercise is best for everyone.

T   F   2. High-impact aerobic dance includes vigorous arm movements while keeping one foot in contact with the ground at all times.

T F 3. Calisthenics are often used for warming up.

T F 4. Weight training is one of the most effective exercise programs for developing muscular strength and muscular endurance.

T F 5. Interval training can be used in swimming as well as jogging.

T F 6. Activities that are highly competitive are usually considered poor stress diversion activities.

T F 7. One disadvantage of swimming for physical fitness is that many injuries occur in this activity.

T F 8. The cardiovascular fitness benefits of swimming are considered to be high.

T F 9. Football is an excellent activity for the development of cardiovascular fitness.

T F 10. Pedaling a bicycle must be done continuously for at least 20 minutes in order to have an aerobic effect.

Discussion

11. What are the advantages of planned exercise programs?

12. Why is walking a very popular form of aerobic exercise?

13. Why should you get physically fit before participating in a sport?

14. What are the factors you should consider when selecting activities for your personal fitness program?

15. What is the value of exercising with a friend?

DESIGNING YOUR OWN PROGRAM 14

Chapter Objectives

As you read this chapter, look for answers to these key questions:

- What are the physical fitness components that you should address when designing your personal fitness program?

- What should you consider when beginning a fitness program?

- What are the steps in designing a personal fitness program?

- What motivational strategies may help you keep your program going?

- After reviewing basic guidelines in initiating a personal fitness program, how would you apply the training principles and concepts in designing a program that will lead to or maintain an optimal level of:

flexibility?	muscular endurance?
cardiovascular fitness?	ideal body weight?
muscular strength?	stress management?

Develop a Total Personal Fitness Program

You cannot hope for success, you've got to plan for it.

When someone talks about a physical fitness program, the image that probably forms in your mind is of someone exercising informally, either running, swimming, or lifting weights. Although each of these activities is a good fitness activity, that image or picture is not a complete one. A single type of vigorous exercise is only one element of a total personal fitness program in which every person should be participating. Your personal program is one that should result in you "looking good" and "feeling good." A well-rounded personal fitness program is made up of several components that require personal lifestyle choices to help you become a winner.

Health-related activities, like bicycling or jogging, will promote fitness of the body systems.

You should consider four specific areas in designing your total personal fitness program: health-related activities, sports skills, stress diversion activities, and good nutrition. Your personal fitness program should include physical activities which meet your needs in each area. Certain activities may meet your needs in more than one area and possibly all four. For example, playing basketball not only provides you with health benefits, but may also serve as a stress diversion activity.

255

Working at an intensity that creates soreness is one of the main reasons why people do not continue with a new exercise program.

Starting Your Program

Many people never stop to think about what is involved in developing a total personal fitness program. They just begin to jog with a friend, or begin to lift weights. This approach usually results in an exercise program that is not beneficial to developing all of the health-related components of physical fitness, and it may not be safe. Many people who begin in this manner may also become sore or injured and stop exercising. Before starting your program, you should think through all the different aspects and make wise decisions. At this point, you should have all the information you need to make these decisions in developing your personal fitness program.

Basic guidelines to follow when beginning a personal fitness program include (a) determine the need for a medical examination, (b) conduct a physical fitness evaluation, (c) set realistic goals, and (d) select activities that help you reach those goals. Keep in mind that you have personal choices to make based on your lifestyle. Your choices should determine your personal fitness program, not the choices of your friends or family.

Above all, you should make sure that your personal fitness program includes all of the health-related components of physical fitness. You must decide if you want to improve each component of physical fitness, or if you only want to improve one or two components while maintaining the others. You may want to gain a few pounds, or you may want to lose a few pounds. Any personal fitness program decision you make should be based on your physical fitness assessment.

Evaluation of your current level of physical fitness is essential for a number of reasons. Once you know what your level of fitness is in each of the health-related components of physical fitness, you will be able to make good decisions, set realistic goals, design an exercise program that will bring about improvement, and use baseline data to judge the amount of improvement you have made by periodic re-evaluation.

Assessment of your current level of physical fitness is important when planning a new program.

An exercise program that will benefit you must follow the principles of training. You should apply the principles of *overload, progression,* and *specificity* that you learned about earlier in this book. Your exercise program should be designed to overload the body system that you want to improve. It must progressively demand more of that body system, and it will only improve the specific part of the body that it was designed to benefit.

Designing Your Personal Fitness Program

Now is the time to begin designing your own personal fitness program. Your current level of physical fitness should be the basis for designing your future program. Use your physical fitness test scores to establish goals. Based on your physical fitness test scores and your goals, begin designing each element of a total personal fitness program. Remember, set realistic goals. If your physical fitness level is very low, it will take time to condition your muscles, ligaments, and other parts of your body to exercise without causing injury.

In order to design a sound personal fitness program, you should follow specific steps. Steps in developing your personal fitness program are:

1. evaluation
2. goal setting
3. selection of activities
4. application of training principles in program design
5. periodic assessment

To help guide you in the process of designing your own program, look at the following example of a typical high school student. Make note of her physical fitness scores, lifestyle, realistic goals, and common-sense approach in meeting those goals.

Sports skills activities like tennis can help you develop motor skills and satisfy your need for competition, but they may also contribute to health-related fitness if your skill level allows you to play hard enough.

Steps in Designing Vanessa's Personal Fitness Program

Vanessa was a fifteen-year-old ninth grader who had never been very active. She spent a lot of time watching television, wishing she had the energy to learn how to play tennis and participate in some of the other activities her classmates enjoy. Even though Vanessa enjoyed swimming, she was a little overweight and felt self-conscious in a bathing suit.

Evaluation

All students in physical education classes were given a physical fitness test during the first two weeks of school. Vanessa recorded her physical fitness test scores on the form provided: (a) cardiovascular fitness-mile run, 14:00 minutes; (b) flexibility, 18 cm; (c) sit-ups, 17; (d) pull-ups, 0; (e) body composition, 44 mm.

NAME __Vanessa__ AGE _15_ CLASS _2ⁿᵈ Period_

Body Weight: _____ pounds _____ kilograms Height: _____ feet/inches _____ meters

Fitness Components	Test Item	Test #1 Date	Health Fitness Standard	Goal	Test #2 Date
Flexibility	Sit and Reach	18cm	25cm	24cm	_____
Cardiovascular	One-Mile Run	1400	10 30	10 30	_____
Abdominal Strength/Endurance	Sit-ups	17	34	37	_____
Upper Body Strength/Endurance	Pull-ups	0	1	1	_____
Body Composition	Skinfolds 1. Tricep	29	_____	_____	_____
	2. Calf	15	_____	_____	_____
	Sum of 1 & 2	44mm	15-35	34	_____

Goal setting

After the class had taken the first physical fitness test, Vanessa's teacher sat down with the students and talked about setting personal goals. The teacher emphasized that the students should only compare their results to themselves. This sparked an interest in Vanessa because she thought she could be successful if all she had to do was compete with herself.

With help from the teacher, Vanessa developed both short-term and long-term goals to provide direction for her personal fitness program. As the final step in goal setting, she wrote down what she thought would be the benefits of accomplishing these goals. Vanessa listed:

1. improved appearance
2. improved self-concept
3. better posture
4. improved cardiovascular endurance
5. improved muscular endurance
6. improved upper body strength

To keep herself motivated, Vanessa made a poster for her room listing the benefits she would obtain from her personal fitness program.

Selection of activities

The next step for Vanessa was to decide on activities in which she would like to participate. Using the Exercise Programs and Sports Activities Analysis Charts in Chapter 13, Vanessa compared the health-related benefits of each activity to her physical fitness goals. For example, Vanessa wanted to improve her cardiovascular fitness and reviewed those activities that were rated high in this component of physical fitness. Vanessa then considered her personality, attitudes,

Evaluation of Activities

NAME Vanessa   AGE   15   CLASS   Second Period

Activities	HR/SR	Components				
		CV	Flex	Mus Str	Mus End	Body Com
Riding Bicycle	HR	X			some	same
Walk/Jog	HR	X			X	X
Stretching Exercise	HR		X			
Negative Pullups	HR			X	X	
Sit-ups	HR			X	X	

cost of activities, availability of facilities, and environmental conditions under which she would exercise. Based on all these factors, Vanessa selected activities that would help her reach her personal fitness goals.

Application of training principles in designing a program

Vanessa's next step was to apply the training principles to the activities she had selected. Using the information she had learned in class, Vanessa was able to personalize her program by applying the principles of overload, progression, and specificity.

cardiovascular

Test Score: Mile Run = 14:00 minutes
Goal: To run the mile run in 10 minutes, 30 seconds on the post-test

Vanessa first designed an exercise program that would help her improve cardiovascular fitness. She decided to ride her bicycle to school each day, rather than ride in the car with her father. She did not expect to ride her bicycle at a pace that would allow her heart rate to reach the lower level of her target heart rate zone of 137 beats per minute. Nor would the one-mile distance provide her sufficient time for aerobic training. However, riding the one mile to and from school each day would help improve muscular endurance in her legs and help toward her cardiovascular fitness goal.

She had learned that she needed to exercise at least three days a week (frequency) at 50 to 85 percent of her maximum heart rate (intensity) for at least 20 minutes (time) to obtain all of the aerobic benefits. Vanessa decided she would walk/jog three days a week as soon as she got home from school. Her plan was to begin slowly, since she knew she was not in very good condition, based on her physical fitness test score. Therefore, in designing her program, she would have to start with low intensity for a short period of time.

Walking and jogging are excellent cardiovascular exercises.

Her goal for the first two weeks would be to walk one mile as fast as she could (intensity). After the first two weeks, she would begin to walk and jog one mile, and then continue walking until she had been exercising for thirty minutes (time). She decided to jog slowly for one block, walk fast for one block, and continue alternating jogging and walking for the one mile. She would do this for at least four weeks.

After the four weeks of alternating jogging and walking, Vanessa decided she would be in good enough shape to try to jog for a full mile, then walk for a short distance, and then jog some more. After completing this routine, she would again continue walking fast until she had exercised for thirty minutes. By the end of three months, she hoped to be able to jog two miles at a steady pace. After she had reached that level of fitness, her goal for the rest of the semester would be to continue exercising for thirty minutes, three days a week, progressively increasing her pace and the distance covered.

Cardiovascular Activity:	Bicycling	Walk/jog
(F) Number of sessions per week	10*	3
(I) Target heart rate for 10 seconds	23–31	24–28
(T) Length of session	1 mile / 10 mins.	30 mins.

*Includes riding to and from school five days a week.

flexibility

Test Score: Sit-and-Reach Test = 18 cm
Goal: To obtain a score of 24 cm on the post-test

Vanessa next looked at flexibility. She would simply have to do stretching exercises, since she was not skilled at any other type of activity that might improve her flexibility. Her initial goal was to improve her fitness test score in the sit-and-reach test. Her teacher had

Stretching exercises should be included in your exercise program not only to improve flexibility, but as part of your warm-up and cool-down to reduce the chance of injury or soreness.

told them in class that people should warm up by stretching before they exercise, and then repeat those same exercises in their cool-down. Vanessa decided she might as well do a warm-up, work on her flexibility and cool-down in each workout session.

She decided to add a five-minute stretching session (time) to her warm-up and cool-down for all five days (frequency) of planned exercise. She selected 10 stretching exercises and planned on holding each one for 15 seconds. Each exercise would be performed for one repetition for three sets. Her goal would be to work toward holding the stretches longer and hopefully, to be able to do 30-second stretches by the end of the semester.

Flexibility Activity:	Routine of 10 static stretches
(F) Number of sessions per week	10 *
(I) Length of stretch	point of slight discomfort
(T) Time of stretch	15 sec./3 sets/per exercise

*Includes warm-up and cool-down five days a week.

muscular strength

Test Score: Pull-ups = 0
Goal: To be able to perform 1 pull-up by the post-test.

Vanessa's teacher had told her that she should place more emphasis on muscular endurance than on muscular strength if she wanted to improve muscle tone and decrease her percentage of body fat. However, since Vanessa was unable to perform even one pull-up on the physical fitness test, she did want to improve her arm strength. Vanessa realized she had a long way to go before she could lift her body weight. Vanessa's teacher had described different exercises, including weight training, that could be used to improve her muscular strength.

Negative pull-ups are another way of developing upper body strength if you cannot perform regular pull-ups. Start in a full pull-up position and slowly lower yourself, using a 5–10 second count. Make your muscles work against gravity's pull on your body weight.

Vanessa also realized she was going to have to exercise at school, since she did not have any way to do pull-ups at home. Vanessa decided to use negative pull-ups to help her reach her goal of one pull-up.

Vanessa decided to work on this component of physical fitness each day at the beginning of class (frequency). She would begin by doing negative pull-ups, trying to make each last for five seconds (intensity). Vanessa decided to begin by doing three negative pull-ups and trying to work up to five (time).

Muscular Strength Activity:	Negative Pull-ups
(F) Number of sessions per week	5
(I) Resistance	Body Weight / 5 second count
(T) Length of session	3–5 repetitions

muscular endurance

Test Score: Sit-ups = 17
Goal: To do 37 by the post-test

Designing a program to help her reach her muscular endurance goal was Vanessa's next task. Vanessa did not believe any of the activities she had picked would help her abdominal muscles. Vanessa decided that the best thing was to do sit-ups, even though she did not enjoy doing them. Vanessa wanted to do as few as possible to reach her goal. She decided to do one set (time) of maximum sit-ups (intensity) three nights a week (frequency) before getting ready for bed. She could monitor her progress, since she had set semester-long goals. Vanessa decided that by the middle of the semester, she needed to have reached 27 sit-ups, or she would make an adjustment in her activity level. Her physical education teacher supported her decision.

Sit-ups, like push-ups, may be modified in different ways to increase or decrease their difficulty.

Muscular Endurance Activity:	Sit-ups
(F) Number of sessions per week	3
(I) Resistance	Body weight using regular sit-ups
(T) Length of session	1 set of maximum sit-ups

Test Score: Skin fold measurement = 44 mm
Goal: To have a body composition measurement of 34 mm by the time of the post-test

Body composition was the last component of physical fitness Vanessa had to address with her personal fitness program. Vanessa liked to eat, but she knew she had to cut down on her intake a little. She was presently consuming an average of 2,400 calories per day, or 16,800 per week. However, Vanessa's daily activity level only required 2,143 calories, or 15,000 per week. The extra 1,800 calories per week were being stored in her body as fat.

Since she presently layed around and watched a lot of television, the exercise program that she had designed would help her body composition. Vanessa tried to think of how she could cut calories without eliminating any of the foods she liked to eat. Vanessa got an idea after reading some examples that her teacher had handed out. Why not just cut out the butter and mayonnaise that she used every day? After all, one little pat of butter had 70 calories, and one spoonful of mayonnaise had 100 calories. Vanessa determined that, on the average, she could reduce her caloric intake by 200 calories per day without giving up any food. She liked that idea.

The personal fitness program that Vanessa had designed would greatly improve her body composition. Even though Vanessa occasionally engaged in physical activity, she did not burn as many calories as she took in. Using the calorie expenditure formula and the chart on Caloric Costs of Activities in Chapter 10, Vanessa calculated that she would burn an additional 272 calories per day, or approximately 1,900 calories per week. This would result in her expending 1,500 calories more than she took in.

Body Composition

Calories Taken In		Calories Burned	
Present # of Calories consumed each week	16,800	Present # of Calories burned each week	− 15,000
Planned Calorie reduction each week	− 1,400	Additional Calories burned in exercise	− 1,900
	15,400		− 16,900
Total excess Calories burned each week = 1,500 caloric reduction			

The excess calories burned each week and the planned calorie reduction would allow Vanessa to lose one-half pound of body weight per week or approximately two pounds per month. During the next sixteen weeks, Vanessa would lose eight pounds, or approximately 26 pounds in one year. One year seemed a long way off. But Vanessa had learned in class that if she wanted to permanently lose body weight, she had to change her lifestyle and not depend on fad diets.

Vanessa's grades were above average, and her home life was stable. She got along with her brother and sisters fairly well, and she found it easy to talk with her parents. What stress Vanessa did have was a result of her interaction with her peers. Since many of the activities in her personal fitness program were stress diversion activities, Vanessa would use those activities for relaxation. She would also use the benefits of improved fitness to manage her stress. In addition, she had identified some of her weaknesses and had developed goals and a plan of action for self-improvement.

Stress diversion activities, like sailing, help individuals relax and manage stress. These activities should be a regular part of everyone's lifestyle.

Periodic assessment

Vanessa built short-term goals into her program that could be used as "targets" to help her periodically assess her progress toward her long-term goals for each component of fitness. She would time herself in the mile run halfway through the semester, with her goal being 12:15. This would put her halfway to her long-term goal of being able to complete the mile run in 10:30.

In order to test her flexibility, Vanessa asked her physical education teacher if she could use the sit-and-reach box occasionally to test her progress. She decided to check her flexibility once a month. She knew her goal was slightly more than touching her toes. This information allowed her to monitor her rate of improvement without the use of the sit-and-reach box.

Vanessa had a long way to go before reaching her ultimate goal of being able to do one pull-up on the physical fitness test. She decided that she would try to do a regular pull-up once a week, prior to doing her sets of negative pull-ups.

The sit-up workouts were self-testing, since she was doing the maximum number she could perform. She would be able to determine her progress each day.

With body composition, Vanessa knew she had a long way to go. She decided to use a combination of ways to monitor her body composition. She would weigh herself once a week, use the mirror test, ask her teacher to take her skin fold once a month, and let how her clothes fit serve as the final judge.

Vanessa understood the importance of managing stress. She set aside thirty minutes each week to evaluate her stress level. Reflecting on the week's activities would allow her to make modifications in her stress management program.

This was going to be a lot of record keeping, but Vanessa thought that it could be fun and that she would be successful. Vanessa and her physical education teacher thought that the goals she had set were realistic and challenging. Her teacher also agreed that the planned personal fitness program would allow her to reach those goals. Vanessa was not sure she could do it, but one thing was certain, she was tired of being embarrassed because she was in such poor condition. At least this was her program, her goals, and she was only competing against herself.

Keep It Going

Starting an exercise program is not difficult. People do that every day. In fact, it is so easy that some individuals will start a program six to ten times a year. The problem is continuing the program once you begin, making it a part of your lifestyle. This problem is almost always a mental, seldom a physical one.

Fight boredom with variety

Boredom is possibly the biggest threat to an exercise program. You must build into your program those things which will continue to interest you and motivate you to exercise regularly. Variety is a must, whether it is a variety of activities, the variety of people with whom you exercise, or the variety of places you exercise. If you only want to jog, you may want to jog different distances over different courses, and maybe at different times of the day.

Exercise with a friend

Most people are sociable individuals and like the social interaction provided by certain types of exercise. Ride your bike with people you enjoy being around. Play tennis with people whose company you enjoy. The bottom line is that people are going to engage in social activities, so make your self-improvement program a social activity whenever possible.

Record keeping

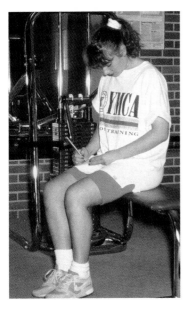

Record keeping should be used on a regular basis to monitor progress and to serve as a motivator so that you stick with your exercise program.

Record keeping and periodic evaluation can also prove to be motivating. You should not depend on remembering the amount of weight lifted, number of repetitions completed, distance covered, or elapsed time. Writing down your performance provides you with objective measurements to help you monitor your progress. Your records will help you in setting new goals, modifying your program, and avoiding injuries. The type of information that you might want to record includes date, number of repetitions and sets, resistance, resting heart rate, exercise heart rate, distance covered, time required, distance for week, and cumulative distance since the program was started.

You might want to test your skills periodically against people who are better than you. Enter a road race, a tennis tournament, or a racquetball tournament. Compare the results with your previous efforts to determine how you are doing.

Make a commitment to "looking good and feeling good." Make a commitment to exercising on a regular basis. Make lifestyle choices that will make you a winner.

Summary

A total fitness program should involve physical activities that meet personal needs in four areas: (a) health-related, (b) sports skills, (c) nutrition, and (d) stress management. When making decisions about your personal program, you must take a number of factors, including assessment of your present level of physical fitness, into account. You may want to design a program for improving specific health-related components of physical fitness, while your test results may show you only need to maintain others.

You should follow five basic steps before beginning your physical fitness program: (a) evaluate your present level of physical fitness, (b) set goals, (c) select activities needed to improve your level of physical fitness, (d) design your fitness program based on the training principles, and (e) plan periodic assessment of your progress.

Start a physical fitness program and continue to make it a part of your everyday routine. Fight boredom by participating in a variety of activities with others. To be a winner, make a commitment to lifestyle choices which will aid you in **looking good and feeling good.**

Study Questions

Vocabulary matching

Place the letter of the correct answer in the place provided.

_____ 1. Body composition

_____ 2. Cardiovascular fitness

_____ 3. Time

_____ 4. Flexibility

_____ 5. Health-related fitness

_____ 6. Intensity

_____ 7. Lifestyle choices

_____ 8. Sports skills activities

_____ 9. Stress diversion activities

_____ 10. Total fitness

A. Activities that help people relax

B. Range of motion in your joints

C. Includes health-related components, skill-related components, and stress management

D. Concerned with the proper functioning of the body systems

E. Condition of the heart and lungs

F. How long you exercise

G. Decisions made about how you live

H. How hard you work

I. Activities that help you develop skill

J. Ratio of fat to muscle, bone, and other tissue

True–false

Circle "T" for all correct statements and "F" for all incorrect ones.

T   F   11. A total personal fitness program includes only those activities that are vigorous in nature.

T   F   12. Activities that are highly competitive are good stress diversion activities.

T F 13. A physical fitness program can be designed to help you either gain or lose weight.

T F 14. Your physical fitness program should be just like your friend's program.

T F 15. A medical exam is **not** necessary unless you have a health problem or you are an adult.

T F 16. Evaluation of your physical fitness level is not really important at the beginning of your program but will be important later on to determine progress.

T F 17. Goal setting is an important key to a successful personal fitness program.

T F 18. Warm-up and cool-down are only important for adults who have not been exercising.

T F 19. Intensity and frequency of your exercise program are important aspects in designing a program.

T F 20. Boredom is the biggest threat to an exercise program.

Discussion

21. What are the key decisions you should make before beginning a personal fitness program?

22. How should health-related activities, sports skill activities, and stress diversion activities be used in developing your total personal fitness program?

23. What basic guidelines should be used in developing your personal fitness program?

24. Identify and explain the key steps that you should go through in designing your personal fitness program.

25. What should you do to motivate yourself to continue your personal fitness program?

BIBLIOGRAPHY

Allsen, P. E., Harrison, J. M. and Vance, B. (1993). *Fitness For Life: An Individualized Approach.* Dubuque, Wm. C. Brown Publishers.

Alter, Michael J. (1990). *Sport Stretch.* Champaign, IL: Leisure Press.

American College of Sports Medicine. (1990). "The Recommended Quantity and Quality of Exercise for Developing and Maintaining Cardiorespiratory and Muscular Fitness in Healthy Adults." *Medicine and Science in Sports and Exercise.* 22:265–274.

American Heart Association. (1992). *1993 Heart and Stroke Facts Statistics.* Dallas, TX: The American Heart Association.

Ardell, D. B. and Tager, M. J. (1989). *Planning For Wellness.* Dubuque, Kendall/Hunt Publishing Company.

Branner, T. T. (1989). *The Safe Exercise Handbook.* Dubuque, Kendall/Hunt Publishing Company.

Bucher, C. A. and Prentice, W. E. (1985). *Fitness For College and Life.* St. Louis, Times Mirror/Mosby College Publishing.

Coleman, E. L. (1992). *Eating for Endurance.* Palo Alto, CA: Bull Publishing.

Cundiff, D. E. and Brynteson, P. (1984). *Health Fitness: Guide To A Life-Style.* Dubuque, Kendall/Hunt Publishing Company.

Davis, J. B. and Knight, E. L. (1985). *CVR Fitness: A Basic Guide For Cardio-Vascular Respiratory Exercise.* Dubuque, Kendall/Hunt Publishing Company.

De Lorme, R. and Stransky, F. (1990). *Fitness and Fallacies.* Dubuque, Kendall/Hunt Publishing Company.

De Vries, H. A. (1986). *Physiology of Exercise for Physical Education and Athletics.* Dubuque, Wm. C. Brown Publishers.

Donovan, G., McNamara, J. and Gianoli, P. (1988). *Exercise Dangers.* Dubuque, Kendall/Hunt Publishing Company.

Frank, B. D. and Howley, E. T. (1989). *Fitness Facts: The Healthy Living Handbook.* Champagne, Human Kinetics.

Frank, B. D. and Howley, E. T. (1989). *Fitness Leader's Handbook.* Champaign, Human Kinetics.

Fox, E. L., R. W. Bowers, and Foss, M. L. (1993). *The Physiological Basis for Exercise and Sport.* Philadelphia: Saunders College Publishing.

Girandola, R. N. (1987). *Running for Lifelong Fitness.* Englewood Cliffs, Prentice-Hall Publishing Company.

Greenberg, J. S. (1987). *Comprehensive Stress Management.* Dubuque, Wm. C. Brown Publishers.

Greenberg, J. S and Pargman, D. (1989). *Physical Fitness: A Wellness Approach.* Englewood Cliffs, Prentice-Hall, Inc.

Hatfield, F. C. and Krotee, M. (1984). *Personalized Weight Training For Fitness & Athletics.* Dubuque, Kendall/Hunt Publishing Company.

Healthy People 2000 Objectives and The National Education Goals. (1992). *Public Health Reports* 107(1):9–14.

Heyward, V. H. (1984). *Designs For Fitness.* Minneapolis, Burgess Publishing Company.

Hockey, R. V. (1989). *Physical Fitness, The Pathway To Healthful Living.* St. Louis, Times Mirror/Mosby College Publishing.

Hoeger, W. (1989). *Lifetime Physical Fitness and Wellness.* Englewood, Morton Publishing Company.

Jackson, A. S., and Pollock, M. L. (1985). Practical Assessment of Body Composition. *The Physician and Sports Medicine*. 13:76–90.

Knight, E. L. and Davis, J. B. (1984). *Flexibility: The Concept of Stretching and Exercise*. Dubuque, Kendall/Hunt Publishing Company.

Kraemer, William J., and Steven, J. F. (1993). *Strength Training for Young Athletes*. Champaign, IL: Human Kinetics Publishers.

Mazzeo, K. S. (1985). *A Commitment to Fitness*. Englewood, Morton Publishing Company.

McArdele, W. D., Katch, F. I. and Katch, V. L. (1986). *Exercise Physiology: Energy, Nutrition, and Human Performance*. Philadelphia, Lea and Febiger.

Melograno, V. J. and Klinzing, J. E. (1988). *An Orientation to Total Fitness*. Dubuque, Kendall/Hunt Publishing Company.

Miller, D. K. and Allen, T. E. (1986). *Fitness: A Lifetime Commitment*. Minneapolis, Burgess Publishing Company.

Prevention Magazine. The Prevention Index 1993: (1993). A Report Card on The Nation's Health. Emmarus, PA: *Prevention Magazine*.

Schroeder, Richard (1990). *Assessing Fitness: Your Guide to a Healthy Lifestyle*. Dubuque, Kendall/Hunt Publishing Company.

Smart Moves. (1990). Orlando, Dairy and Food Nutrition Council of Florida.

Thygerson, A. L. (1989). *Fitness and Health: Lifestyle Strategies*. Boston, Jones and Bartlett.

GLOSSARY

A

adipose tissue —fat or fat tissue
adrenaline —chemical secreted by the adrenal glands which moves the body into the fight or flight response
aerobic —with oxygen
agility —ability to change the position of the body and to control the movement of the whole body
anabolic steroids —synthetic version of the male sex hormone, testosterone
anaerobic —without oxygen
anorexia nervosa —disorder in which a person refuses to eat normally, resulting in extreme thinness and even starvation
artery —a vessel that carries blood away from the heart
atherosclerosis —condition in which fatty deposits build up on inner walls of arteries, causing narrowing of the arterial passageway
atrophy —the wasting away or decrease in size of a body part, particularly muscle

B

balance —ability to keep an upright posture while standing still or moving
ballistic stretching — stretching that involves bobbing, bouncing or jerky movements which use the body's momentum
basal metabolism —amount of energy required to maintain one's body at rest
blood pressure —measure of blood force against the walls of the arteries
body composition —ratio of fat to muscle, bone, and other body tissues
body image —the way a person sees his or her physical self
bulimia —eating disorder characterized by overeating followed by self-induced vomiting, use of laxatives, or very strenuous exercise to avoid weight gain

C

calisthenics—exercises that use one's body weight as resistance

calorie—amount of energy needed to raise the temperature of one kilogram of water one degree centigrade; unit that measures the energy in foods

capillary—a network of small vessels located between the arteries and veins in which exchanges of vital substances occur between tissue and blood

carbohydrates—essential nutrients that are the body's primary source of energy

cardiovascular fitness—ability of the heart, blood vessels, and respiratory system to supply oxygen and nutrients to the muscles during exercise

carotid artery—a major artery located on each side of the neck allowing blood to flow from the aorta to the head

cholesterol—a waxy, fat-like substance found in animal tissue

circuit training—an exercise program in which one makes one or more trips around a prescribed course, stopping at each station to perform a specified exercise

circulatory system—primarily consisting of the blood, heart, and blood vessels

consumer—person who buys goods and services

cool-down—a 10- to 15-minute period of mild exercise following vigorous exercise that allows the body and heart rate to return to normal

coordination—integration of eye, hand, and foot movements

creeping obesity—gaining of fat very slowly over a period of years

criterion-referenced tests—physical fitness tests that use specific standards to judge fitness levels

D

dehydration—loss of water from body tissues

diaphragm—a large muscle in the upper abdomen

diastolic blood pressure—the blood pressure during the relaxation phase of the heart cycle

distress—negative stress resulting from something bad

diuretics—drugs used to control accumulation of fluids in body tissues, congestive heart failure, and high blood pressure

dynamic stretching—stretching done in continuous, slow, and controlled manner

E

ectomorph—body type with a slender, slight build

endomorph—body type with a large, soft, bulging body and a pear-shaped appearance

eustress—positive stress resulting from something good

F

fad diets —diets that promote weight loss without sound nutritional practices

fast-twitch fibers —white muscle fibers that contract quickly, allowing explosive muscular contractions

fat-soluble vitamins —vitamins that can be stored in fat deposits in the body; vitamins A, D, E, and K

fight or flight response —involuntary physical response to a stressor that gives an individual the capacity for sudden and quick action

F.I.T. —the three ways to achieve overload in a physical fitness program —frequency, intensity, and time

flexibility —the range of movement possible at various joints

four basic food groups —grouping of foods that allows one to select the proper foods for a balanced diet

frequency —how often one should exercise to improve a component of physical fitness

G

goal setting —process designed to motivate people to make changes in their lifestyles and increase self-improvement

general stressors —types of stimuli that trigger the stress response but are not easily identifiable by the body

H

HDL —high density lipoprotein which helps remove excess cholesterol

health-related fitness —components of physical fitness that contribute to how well the systems of the body operate

health-related fitness standards —satisfactory levels of flexibility, cardiovascular fitness, muscular strength and endurance, and body composition needed for good health

health risk factors —factors associated with disease, disability, and premature death

heart attack —when heart tissue is damaged or dies as a result of not receiving a sufficient blood supply

heat cramps —heat-related problem in which certain muscles contract involuntarily and cause pain

heat exhaustion —condition characterized by profuse sweating, dizziness, and extreme weakness

heat stroke —medical emergency characterized by hot, dry skin and a rising body temperature

high-impact aerobics —aerobic dance that includes jumping, bouncing, and running

homeostasis —internal balance of the body

hypertension —commonly called high blood pressure; an unstable or persistent elevation of blood pressure above normal range

hyperthermia—an increase in body temperature with a reduction of body fluids

hypothermia—excessive decline in body temperature

I

ideal body weight—how much a person would weigh if he or she had an appropriate percentage of body fat

inactivity—lack of physical activity and exercise

intensity—how hard one should exercise to improve fitness

interval training—exercise program that involves a series of exercises interspersed with rest periods

isokinetic exercises—exercises with special machines that allow for the maximum resistance over the complete range of motion

isometric exercises—exercises in which one contracts muscles but does not move body parts

isostatic stretching—form of stretching in which a partner pushes the body beyond the initial limit

isotonic exercises—exercises in which a muscle lengthens and shortens through its full range of movement while lowering and raising a resistance

L

lactic acid—a waste product built up in the body as a result of severe muscular exercise

LDL—low density lipoprotein which leads to a buildup of cholesterol on artery walls

lean body mass—mass of the body made up of muscle tissue and other non-fat tissue such as bones, ligaments, and tendons

lifetime sports—individual sports that can be engaged in for a lifetime

ligament—strong, fibrous tissue which attaches one bone to another

long-term goals—goals that take a long time, perhaps years, to reach

low-impact aerobics—aerobic dance that includes vigorous arm movements while keeping one foot in contact with the ground at all times

M

maximum heart rate—heart rate that should not be exceeded during exercise; found by substracting one's age from 220

media—newspapers, magazines, television, and radio

mesomorph—body type with a solid, muscular, and large-boned physique

minerals—essential nutrients needed in small amounts to prevent deficiencies and diseases in the body

muscle bound—an imbalanced development of strength between the antagonist and agonist muscle in which a loss of flexibility occurs

muscular endurance—ability to use muscles for a long period of time

muscular strength—ability of muscles to exert a force one time

N

negative coping techniques—those responses that ease or disguise the symptoms of stress and that are harmful to an individual and those around him or her

norm-referenced tests—physical fitness tests that use norms to indicate fitness levels

O

obese—having an excessive amount of body fat

obesity—excessive deposits of fat on the body

overweight—exceeding desirable body weight by 10 percent according to height and weight charts

P

physical fitness—capacity of the whole body to function at optimum efficiency; determined by the condition of the heart and circulatory, respiratory, and muscular systems, degree of flexibility, and percentage of body fat

planned program—pre-determined programs that include specific exercises for persons of specific fitness levels or ages

positive coping strategies—strategies to help deal with stress that cannot be avoided

power—ability to do strength performances at a rapid pace

principle of overload—exposing the muscles, joints, and cardiovascular and respiratory systems to more work and stress than is normally experienced

principle of progression—progressively increasing the level of exercise so that improvement in physical fitness will continue

principle of specificity—doing specific exercises to improve specific components of physical fitness in specific body parts

proteins—essential nutrients needed for growth and repair of body tissues

pulse—caused by pressure of blood on an artery wall; corresponds to heart beat

R

reaction time —amount of time it takes to get moving once the senses signal the need to move

recovery heart rate —heart rate after exercise

red blood cell —the cell that carries oxygen to the tissues

relaxation techniques —activities that reduce muscle tension and stress in the body by concentrated use of the mind

repetition - the completion of a single, full-range movement of the body part being exercised

respiratory system —composed of lungs and air passages that help supply oxygen to the body

resting heart rate —heart rate just after waking in the morning, before getting out of bed

S

saturated fats —fats contained in animal products

set —a group of repetitions performed one after the other

shin splint —an inflammation of the membrane on the front of the bones in the lower leg

short-term goals —goals that can be reached in a short period of time

skill-related fitness —components of physical fitness that contribute to the ability to successfully participate in sports

skinfold caliper —device used to measure a fold of skin and its underlying layer of body fat

slow-twitch fibers —red muscle fibers that are slow to contract but have the ability to continue contracting for long periods of time

somatotype —body type

speed —ability to cover a distance in a short time

sports skills activities —activities that help develop sports skills and satisfy the need for competition

spot reduction —myth that exercising muscles in a particular area of the body will remove fat from that area

static stretching —slowly moving a muscle to its stretching point and holding the position for 15 seconds

stitch-in-the-side —sharp pain in the side just under the ribs

stress —nonspecific response of the body to any demand made upon it

stress diversion activities —those activities, both active and passive, that reduce or divert stress

stressor —events, situations, or activities that cause stress

systolic blood pressure —the blood pressure during the contraction phase of the heart

T

target heart rate —60 to 90 percent of the maximum heart rate; results in greatest cardiovascular benefits from exercise

tendon —soft tissues that anchor muscles to bones

time —how long one exercises to improve fitness

time lines —tools used to organize and plot the course to a major goal

U

unsaturated fats —fats found in plant sources

V

vein —a vessel that carries blood to the heart

W

warm-up —a 10- to 15-minute period during which the body is prepared for vigorous exercise

water-soluble vitamins —vitamins that dissolve in water and cannot be stored in body tissues

INDEX